Dr. P. E. Secker

Dielectrics

MODERN ELECTRICAL STUDIES

A Series Edited by

Professor G. D. SIMS

Head of Department of Electronics
University of Southampton

DIELECTRICS

by J. C. ANDERSON Ph.D.

Reader in Electrical Engineering
Imperial College, London

CHAPMAN AND HALL LTD
11 NEW FETTER LANE LONDON EC4

First published 1964
© *J. C. Anderson* 1964
Printed in Great Britain by
Spottiswoode, Ballantyne & Co Ltd
London and Colchester

Preface

Dielectric materials have not, in recent years, undergone such rapid development as have the related semiconductor materials. Nevertheless there has been a steady and increasing interest in dielectric properties and behaviour. As a result new ferroelectric materials are being discovered, and existing ones have reached the stage of device application. The new mixed titanate ceramics have provided more efficient ultrasonic transducers and promise important contributions in the field of miniaturization of radio communications components. The study of space-charged limited currents in dielectric crystals has led to the solid-state analogue of the vacuum tube, which should provide a useful extension to the range of semiconductor devices. Thin-film capacitors, in which the dielectric is a layer of only one micron thickness, are a practical reality and combine extremely high capacitance with microscopic size. All these and many other developments establish 'Dielectrics' as an important field of study quite on a par, for instance, with magnetic materials or semiconductors. Such status has, in the past, not generally been accorded to the subject, and it is hoped that this book will assist in remedying the situation. It is based upon third-year undergraduate and postgraduate courses of lectures delivered at Imperial College by the author.

The reader requires little beyond a familiarity with elementary electrostatics and with differential calculus, and a brief acquaintance with classical statistics. Knowledge of the j-notation in alternating electric current theory and an acquaintance with vector algebra are also assumed.

The book is specifically aimed at providing a textbook for a third-year undergraduate course in dielectrics for electrical engineers and physicists. It should also provide a useful foundation for third-year chemists and for those biologists concerned with dielectric properties. The coverage has been extended to serve first-year postgraduate students studying in the general field of materials, especially those going on to do research in dielectrics. The m.k.s. system of units is used throughout.

The first chapter provides a brief revision of fundamentals, the second summarizes methods of measurement of permittivity and the third discusses equivalent circuits. The fourth chapter introduces various models for dielectric behaviour, and this leads to the next section of three chapters dealing with formal dielectric theory. The remaining three chapters are devoted to special dielectric properties and their applications and cover the more important modern developments, relating these to the theory. In a book of this length it is not possible to deal fully either with all the refinements of the theoretical models or with all the practical developments of importance. Wherever possible, however, references are given to other books and publications in which the reader can follow up any particular aspect in which he requires further detail.

The author would like to thank Dr P. M. Gundry and Miss E. M. Whitton for reading the manuscript and making many helpful suggestions, and Mr R. Puddy who drew the diagrams.

J. C. A.

Imperial College, 1963

Contents

CHAPTER 1

General Properties

Introduction

The study of dielectric materials sprang from the practical need for insulators, since the early experiments on electrostatics were founded on the isolation of electrostatic charge by dielectric materials which would not conduct the charge away. Amber, bees-wax and glass were amongst the first practically-applied insulating materials. With the advent of current electricity the properties of these materials had to be more closely studied to provide for increasing practical demands and their response to an applied field had to be determined and characterized. For a given material, the insulating properties can be described in terms of the *dielectric strength*, expressed as the field which, when applied to the material, causes an uncontrollable current to flow through or across it.

From the early days of electrostatics the ability of dielectric materials to increase the charge-storage capacity of a condenser was known. Like dielectric strength, this is a macroscopic characteristic to specify which the parameter *dielectric constant*, or *permittivity*, was defined. The applications of high-frequency current electricity, in connexion with radio, increased the demands for condensers of high capacity, high breakdown strength and small size. To meet these requirements many dielectric materials were examined and classified by their dielectric strength and permittivity, with a view to their use in this field, and the demand arose for better materials. Any search for new or improved materials in a particular field, to be successful, demands a knowledge of the fundamental mechanisms involved in their particular properties. It is the job of dielectric theory to provide this knowledge by accounting for macroscopic behaviour, in terms of the atomic and molecular structure of the material.

A complete theoretical account of the dielectric behaviour of all classes of material is a tremendously difficult task and is never likely to be possible. However, by virtue of well-founded, simplifying assumptions, theoretical 'models' of practical dielectrics have been built up. Using these models, theory predicts certain properties or variations of parameters which can be tested experimentally, and the degree of closeness with which the experimental results are predicted is a measure of the success of the model. Once the theoretical model, based on the atomic and molecular structure of the material, is successful it will provide the knowledge on which the search for new materials may be founded and may also be used to deduce the probable behaviour of the dielectric in different electrical environments. In addition, properties may be predicted which have not yet been observed experimentally. As an example of this, the nineteenth-century theories of dielectric behaviour predicted the possibility of spontaneous polarization or 'ferroelectricity', but the first ferroelectric material to be recognized as such was not found until 1935.

In brief, the proper understanding of dielectric behaviour requires an adequate theoretical background as a precursor to discussion of practical application, to the appreciation of new developments and to accounting for abnormal properties in a material. For this reason, the second part of the book is devoted to dielectric theory.

To provide the necessary basis for discussion of the theoretical models, we require a knowledge of basic electrostatic theory on the one hand and a knowledge of the measurement and significance of the macroscopic parameters on the other. These are dealt with in the first part of the book. In this chapter we revise the fundamentals of electrostatic theory.

Coulomb's Law
Experiments on electrically-charged bodies yield the following observations:

(1) Like charges repel and opposite charges attract each other;
(2) The force between the charges is
    (a) inversely proportional to the square of the distance between them
    (b) dependent on the medium in which they are embedded
    (c) acts along the line joining the charges
    (d) is proportional to the product of the charge magnitudes.

These facts are summarized in Coulomb's law which may be stated as:

$$\mathbf{F} = A.\frac{q_1 q_2}{\epsilon r^2}.(\mathbf{a}) \text{ newtons} \qquad (1.1)$$

where $\mathbf{F}$ is defined as the force between the charges and $\mathbf{a}$ is a unit vector pointing from one charge directly *away* from the other. This has the implication that if the two charges q_1 and q_2 are of opposite sign $\mathbf{F}$ is negative. This negative sign attached to $\mathbf{F}$ means that it has the opposite direction to that of $\mathbf{a}$, i.e. it is a force of attraction between the charges.

r is the distance between the charges and ϵ is a property of the medium called its permittivity, accounting for the observation 2(*b*), above.

An alternative formulation of Coulomb's law is to treat $\mathbf{r}$ as a vector so that equation (1.1) may be written as:

$$\mathbf{F} = A\frac{q_1 q_2}{\epsilon r^2}.\frac{\mathbf{r}}{r}$$

$$= A\frac{q_1 q_2}{\epsilon r^3}.\mathbf{r}$$

which has the significance that, if q_1 and q_2 are positive, the force on one charge a distance r from another will be in the direction of r increasing.

A is a constant whose value will depend on the units used for charge, distance and force. In the rationalized m.k.s. system used throughout this book, A has the value $1/4\pi$, i.e.

$$\mathbf{F} = \frac{q_1 q_2}{4\pi \epsilon r^2}(\mathbf{a}) \text{ newtons.} \qquad (1.2)$$

When A is made dimensionless, it necessarily implies units for the permittivity ϵ, which may be found from the appropriate units substituted in (1.2), i.e.

$$\epsilon \equiv \frac{(\text{coulombs})^2}{\text{newtons (metres)}^2}$$

but $\qquad$ newton-metres = joules = $\dfrac{(\text{charge in coulombs})^2}{\text{farads}}$

from the relation for the energy, E joules, in a condenser of capacitance C farads, carrying a charge Q coulombs, $E = \frac{1}{2} \cdot (Q^2/C)$. Thus,

$$\epsilon \equiv \frac{(\text{coulombs})^2}{\text{joules metres}} \equiv \frac{\text{farads}}{\text{metres}}.$$

Electric Field

A charge in the vicinity of a system of charges will, in general, experience a force. The region of influence of the charges is called an electric field, and its strength at a point is defined as the force *per unit charge* on a positive test-charge placed at that point. The electric intensity or 'field strength' will, by definition, be a vector defined by

$$\mathbf{E} = \frac{\mathbf{F}}{\delta q} \tag{1.3}$$

where $\mathbf{F}$ is the force acting on the infinitesimal test-charge δq. Using (1.2) the field arising from a point charge q in a homogeneous dielectric medium of permittivity ϵ will be given by

$$\mathbf{E} = \frac{q}{4\pi\epsilon r^2}(\mathbf{a}). \tag{1.4}$$

Since $\mathbf{a}$ is directed along the line joining q to the unit test-charge in a direction, from q, away from the unit charge, and since $\mathbf{E}$ is defined by the force on a *positive* charge, it follows that the direction of $\mathbf{E}$ will always be *away* from a *positive* charge and *towards* a *negative* charge. This may also be described by stating that $\mathbf{E}$ has the direction in which a free, positive charge would move under its influence. By substitution of the appropriate units in (1.3) the units of E are readily shown to be volts (metre)$^{-1}$.

Electric intensity, or field strength, is an important parameter in electrical engineering, particularly in connexion with the breakdown strengths of insulating materials. To give some examples, a spark will be produced in dry air, at normal atmospheric pressure, when the electric field reaches a strength of approximately 2×10^7 V/m; this is its 'breakdown strength'. A good transformer oil will withstand in the region of 10^8 V/m whilst high vacuum ($\sim 10^{-5}$ mm Hg) has a breakdown strength of around twice this figure.

Electric Flux Density

When a dielectric material is placed in an electric field already existing in a homogeneous medium, such as air, it has the effect of changing the distribution of the field to a degree depending upon its relative permittivity; i.e. the electric field intensity is a function of the medium in which it exists. This is analogous to the introduction of a magnetic material into a magnetic field. The field concentrates in the material to a degree dependent upon its relative permeability, and the field intensity within the material is described by the magnetic flux density, B, in it, defined by the equation $B = \mu H$, where μ is the permeability of the material and H the magnetic field strength.

In a similar way we define an electric flux density, D, by

$$\mathbf{D} = \epsilon \mathbf{E}. \qquad (1.5)$$

The electric flux density arising from a point charge, q, will be given, from (1.4), by

$$\mathbf{D} = \frac{q}{4\pi r^2} (\mathbf{a}) \qquad (1.6)$$

and is thus a function of the charge and its position only, and is not a property of the medium. In the c.g.s. system $\mathbf{D}$ is called the electric displacement and has the same units as field $\mathbf{E}$. In the m.k.s. system the units of $\mathbf{D}$ are found from (1.5) as

$$\frac{\text{farads}}{\text{metres}} \cdot \frac{\text{volts}}{\text{metres}} = \text{coulombs} \cdot (\text{metre})^{-2}.$$

If we take a point r metres from a charge q coulombs, the flux density at that point will, from (1.6), be $q/4\pi r^2$ coulombs per square metre. Taking q to be at the centre of a sphere of r metres' radius, the flux density will be the same at all points on the sphere's surface. The total flux crossing the surface will be given by the product of D and the surface area; i.e.

$$\Psi = \frac{q}{4\pi r^2} \cdot 4\pi r^2 = q \text{ coulombs}$$

and it is seen that the total flux crossing the surface of a sphere with a charge at its centre is equal to the magnitude of the charge, and is independent of the radius of the sphere.

Gauss' Law

The above statement is generalized in Gauss' law which states that, for any closed surface containing a system of charges, the flux out of the surface is equal to the charge enclosed.

Consider a point charge q surrounded by an arbitrary closed surface, S, as illustrated in Fig. 1. The flux density D at any point on the surface will be given by $q/4\pi r^2$.

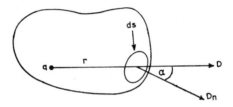

Fig. 1. Gauss' law

Now, imagining the electric flux as a flow across the surface, the amount crossing an elemental area dS will be determined by the component, D_n, of the flux density normal to the surface. Thus, the total flux $d\psi$ crossing dS will be given by

$$d\psi = D_n.dS = D\cos\alpha\,dS = \frac{q\cos\alpha}{4\pi r^2}dS. \qquad (1.7)$$

But $dS\cos\alpha/r^2$ is the solid angle $d\Omega$ subtended at q by the elemental area dS, and the flux is given by $(q/4\pi).d\Omega$. The sum of the flux over the whole surface will be the integral of the solid angle over the whole surface which is simply 4π steradians. The flux is therefore $(q/4\pi).4\pi = q$. Thus we have, for a closed surface S

$$\oint_{S} D\cos\alpha\,dS = q \qquad (1.8)$$

the symbol $\oint_{S}$ indicating integration over the whole of a closed surface.

Since the fluxes due to each charge enclosed are additive at any point on the surface, the total flux across the surface will be due to the sum of the charges enclosed, i.e.

$$\oint_s D \cos \alpha \, dS = \Sigma q \tag{1.9}$$

which is the mathematical statement of Gauss' law.

In vector notation this is equivalent to

$$\oint_s \mathbf{D} . \mathbf{dS} = \Sigma q \tag{1.10}$$

where $\mathbf{dS}$ is an element, of area dS, and orientation defined by the direction of the normal to its surface.

From the foregoing it will be seen that Gauss' law is based on the same experimental facts as is Coulomb's law; it is a form more convenient for certain types of calculation illustrated in the following examples:

A coaxial transmission line comprises an inner conducting cylinder of radius a and an outer of radius b. If the inner conductor carries a charge $+q$ per unit length, the outer will have a charge $-q$ per unit length induced on its inner surface. We may use Gauss' law to determine the field existing in the dielectric medium (of permittivity ϵ) between the conductors.

From the symmetry of the configuration it is clear that the field will be purely radial, will be invariant with angular position about the inner conductor and with distance along the conductor (for an infinitely long line).

To determine the field at a distance r from the axis of the inner conductor, where $a < r < b$, we imagine a cylindrical surface of radius r and length l, closed at the ends whose axis coincides with the inner conductor. From the above symmetry considerations there will be no flux crossing the closed ends, and the flux density $\mathbf{D}$ will everywhere be normal to the cylindrical surface. Thus the total flux crossing the surface will be $D.2\pi rl$ whilst the charge enclosed will be $q.l$, using (1.10)

$$2\pi rlD = lq$$

2

and, if the dielectric medium is homogeneous, $D = \epsilon E$ whence

$$E = \frac{q}{2\pi\epsilon r} \text{ volts/metre.} \tag{1.11}$$

If we consider a point outside the outer conductor, i.e. $r > b$, then the charge enclosed by the imaginary surface will be $(+q-q)l = 0$. Thus the field is zero everywhere outside the outer conductor.

Considering the case of $r < a$, the field inside the inner conductor will also be zero, since charge exists only on the surface of a conductor. As an exercise, however, suppose we consider the inner conductor to be replaced by a region containing distributed charge, such as a beam of electrons, also having radius a. The charge enclosed by the imaginary surface, radius $r < a$, will clearly be the volume integral of charge density, i.e.

$$\oint_S \mathbf{D}.\mathbf{dS} = \int_V \rho \, dV$$

where ρ is the charge per unit volume. In the case of a uniform charge-distribution the volume integral will be simply the charge density multiplied by the volume. In the most general case, however, this will be a triple integral which may only be carried out where the variation of charge density with position is precisely known.

Assuming the electron beam to have a charge uniformly distributed over its cross-section, the imaginary surface of radius r and length l will enclose a charge $\pi r^2 l \rho$, and the field will be given, from (1.11) by

$$2\pi r l \epsilon E = l.\pi r^2 \rho. \tag{1.12}$$

In practice, rather than the charge density we would know the current I, carried by the beam. Now I is the charge per second, passing a given point, and if the beam moves with a velocity, v, a unit length of it would contain charge I/v coulombs. For a radius, a, the charge per unit volume would be

$$\frac{I}{\pi a^2 v}$$

whence, from (1.12),

$$E = \frac{rI}{2\pi a^2 \, \epsilon v} \text{ volts/metre for } r < a.$$

Electrostatic Potential

If a field exists in a medium and a unit point charge is placed in it, the work done on the unit charge in moving between two points A and B is defined as the 'potential difference' between A and B.

Mathematically
$$\phi_A - \phi_B = - \int_B^A \mathbf{E} \cdot \mathbf{dl} \tag{1.13}$$

and the potential difference is a scalar quantity. For this reason it is mathematically much more convenient to deal with than are vector quantities such as $\mathbf{E}$ and $\mathbf{D}$.

Since only difference in potential has been defined, the potential at a given point can only be stated with respect to some other point of known, or arbitrarily fixed, potential. Frequently we define the potential of a point at infinity as zero, so that the potential at a point P, say, would be

$$\phi_P = - \int_\infty^P \mathbf{E} \cdot \mathbf{dl}. \tag{1.14}$$

Suppose that the field at P is due to a charge Q and that we bring a unit charge up from infinity to the point P by any path.

The work done on the unit charge in moving along any infinitesimal portion of path dl will be equal to the product of the path length and the component of field along the path. The total work in moving from infinity will be the integral of this product, i.e.

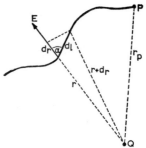

Fig. 2. Electrostatic potential

$$\text{work done} = - \int_\infty^P E \cos \alpha \, dl.$$

Now, referring to Fig. 2, $dl \cos \alpha = dr$ so that the potential at P will be given by

$$\phi_P = - \int_\infty^{r_P} \frac{Q}{4\pi\epsilon r^2} dr = \frac{Q}{4\pi\epsilon r_p}. \tag{1.15}$$

Where there is a system of charges $Q_1 \ldots Q_n$ at distances $r_1 \ldots r_n$, the total potential at P will be

$$\phi_P = \sum_{i=1}^{n} \frac{Q_i}{4\pi\epsilon r_i} \qquad (1.16)$$

or, for the generalized case of a distributed charge of density ρ,

$$\phi = \int_V \frac{\rho \, dV}{4\pi\epsilon r} \qquad (1.17)$$

where r will be the distance between the centre of gravity of the charge and the point considered.

Since the capacitance of a condenser is defined as the ratio of charge on it to the potential difference between the electrodes, the above type of calculation can be used to find the capacitance of a two-electrode system.

As an example we may consider the coaxial transmission line dealt with previously. The potential difference between the coaxial cylinders will be given by

$$\phi_a - \phi_b = - \int_b^a E_r \, dr$$

since the field is entirely radial. Using the value of E_r from (1.11)

$$\phi_a - \phi_b = - \int_b^a \frac{q}{2\pi\epsilon r} \, dr$$

$$= \frac{q}{2\pi\epsilon} \log\left(\frac{b}{a}\right)$$

thus capacitance per unit length is

$$C = \frac{q}{\phi_a - \phi_b} = \frac{2\pi\epsilon}{\log\left(\dfrac{b}{a}\right)} \text{ farads/metre.}$$

Field and Potential

In general, from the definition of potential difference we may write

$$d\phi = -\mathbf{E}.\mathbf{dl}$$

where $d\phi$ is the p.d. between two points dl apart. Now $\mathbf{dl}$ may be written in terms of its components and unit vectors $\mathbf{i}$, $\mathbf{j}$ and $\mathbf{k}$;

$$\mathbf{dl} = dx.\mathbf{i} + dy.\mathbf{j} + dz.\mathbf{k}$$

as also can be the field E, so that

$$d\phi = -(E_x.\mathbf{i} + E_y.\mathbf{j} + E_z.\mathbf{k})(dx.\mathbf{i} + dy.\mathbf{j} + dz.\mathbf{k}).$$

Multiplying term by term we get products of the type $E_x dx.\mathbf{i}.\mathbf{i}$ and, since $\mathbf{i}$ is a *unit* vector, this is simply $E_x dx$. For terms involving products like $\mathbf{i}.\mathbf{j}$, the value will be zero, since $\mathbf{i}$ and $\mathbf{j}$ have an angle of 90° between them, and their modulus is ij cos 90. Thus we have

$$d\phi = -(E_x dx + E_y dy + E_z dz). \tag{1.18}$$

Now ϕ is a function of x, y and z, and its total derivative may be written by Taylor's theorem as

$$d\phi = \frac{\partial \phi}{\partial x}dx + \frac{\partial \phi}{\partial y}dy + \frac{\partial \phi}{\partial z}dz. \tag{1.19}$$

Comparing this with (1.18) we have

$$\mathbf{E} = -\left(\frac{\partial \phi}{\partial x}\mathbf{i} + \frac{\partial \phi}{\partial y}\mathbf{j} + \frac{\partial \phi}{\partial z}\mathbf{k}\right) \tag{1.20}$$

which in vector notation, is simply

$$\mathbf{E} = -\operatorname{grad}\phi = -\nabla\phi \tag{1.21}$$

where the del operator, ∇, represents the operation

$$\mathbf{i}\frac{\partial}{\partial x} + \mathbf{j}\frac{\partial}{\partial y} + \mathbf{k}\frac{\partial}{\partial z}.$$

Thus the field is the gradient of the potential, meaning that it is a vector showing the magnitude and direction of the maximum space variation of the potential, ϕ, at any point.

Poisson's Equation

For a region containing a distributed charge, ρ per unit volume, Gauss' law may be written as

$$\oint_S \epsilon\mathbf{E}.\mathbf{ds} = \int_V \rho\,dV. \tag{1.22}$$

Consider an elementary volume $dV = dx\,dy\,dz$ in Cartesian co-ordinates containing a distributed charge ρ per unit volume, and let this be in a field $\mathbf{E}$ whose components are Ex, Ey and Ez as shown in

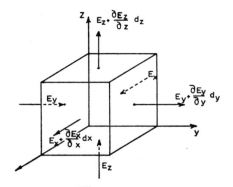

Fig. 3. Poisson's equation

Fig. 3. The field strength will change between each pair of opposite faces of the cube, so that if the field into one face is, say, E_x, that at the opposite face will be $E_x + (\partial E_x/\partial x)\,dx$ as shown in the diagram.

The total normal flux emerging from the cube will therefore be given by taking the difference between the flux density times area over each pair of faces. Thus the total flux out in the x-direction will be

$$\epsilon\left(E_x.dy\,dz + \frac{\partial E_x}{\partial x}dx.dy\,dz - E_x.dy\,dz\right)$$

and similarly for the other directions. Thus total flux out will be

$$\epsilon\left(\frac{\partial E_x}{\partial x} + \frac{\partial E_y}{\partial y} + \frac{\partial E_z}{\partial z}\right)dx\,dy\,dz.$$

Using (1.22) we have

$$\oint_{s} \epsilon \mathbf{E} . \mathbf{ds} = \epsilon \left(\frac{\partial E_x}{\partial x} + \frac{\partial E_y}{\partial y} + \frac{\partial E_z}{\partial z} \right) dV = \rho \, dV \qquad (1.23)$$

assuming the charge density ρ to be constant over the elementary volume dV.

In vector notation

$$\frac{\partial E_x}{\partial x} + \frac{\partial E_y}{\partial y} + \frac{\partial E_z}{\partial z} = \text{div} \, \mathbf{E} = \nabla . \mathbf{E}$$

and is the divergence of the field. Thus (1.23) may be written as

$$\nabla . \mathbf{E} = \frac{\rho}{\epsilon} \qquad (1.24)$$

and Gauss' theorem may be restated as Gauss' divergence theorem

$$\oint_{s} \mathbf{E} . \mathbf{ds} = \int_{V} \nabla . \mathbf{E} \, dV. \qquad (1.25)$$

From equation (1.21) $\mathbf{E} = -\nabla \phi$, and using this we have Poisson's equation

$$\nabla . \nabla \phi = -\frac{\rho}{\epsilon} \quad \text{or} \quad \nabla^2 \phi = -\frac{\rho}{\epsilon}. \qquad (1.26)$$

For charge-free region, where $\rho = 0$, this reduces to Laplace's equation

$$\nabla^2 \phi = 0 \qquad (1.27)$$

where the del-squared operator ∇^2 represents the operation

$$\frac{\partial^2}{\partial x^2} + \frac{\partial^2}{\partial y^2} + \frac{\partial^2}{\partial z^2}.$$

This operation may be transferred to other co-ordinates, and this is sometimes required for particular problems. In cylindrical co-ordinates (ρ, z, ψ)

$$\nabla^2 \phi = \frac{\partial^2 \phi}{\partial \rho^2} + \frac{1}{\rho} \frac{\partial \phi}{\partial \rho} + \frac{1}{\rho^2} \frac{\partial^2 \phi}{\partial \psi^2} + \frac{\partial^2 \phi}{\partial z^2}$$

and in spherical co-ordinates (r, θ, ψ)

$$\nabla^2 \phi = \frac{1}{r^2} \frac{\partial}{\partial r}\left(r^2 \frac{\partial \phi}{\partial r}\right) + \frac{1}{r^2 \sin^2 \theta} \frac{\partial^2 \phi}{\partial \psi^2} + \frac{1}{r^2 \sin \theta} \frac{\partial}{\partial \theta}\left(\sin \theta \frac{\partial \phi}{\partial \theta}\right). \quad (1.28)$$

An example of the application of Laplace's equation will be found in Chapter 6.

Permittivity of Free Space

Consider a capacitor comprising rectangular, parallel plates of area a (metres)^2 each a distance d metres apart in vacuum. Let Q be the charge in coulombs due to a p.d. of V volts between the plates. If we neglect fringing effects at the edges of the plates, the electric flux lines will travel straight across from one plate to the other, and the electric field strength, E, between the plates will be V/d Volts/m.

In the rationalized m.k.s. system of units it is assumed that one line of electric flux emanates from a charge of 1 coulomb. Thus there will be Q lines of flux between the plates and the electric flux density, D, will be given by Q/a coulombs (metre)$^{-2}$.

Now from the definition of equation (1.5), permittivity is the ratio of flux density to field, and using the foregoing arguments

$$\epsilon = \frac{D}{E} = \frac{Q/a}{V/d} \quad (1.29)$$

but $Q/V = C$, where C is capacitance in farads,

$$\therefore \qquad \epsilon = \frac{Cd}{a} \text{ farads/metre} \quad (1.30)$$

For the case of a vacuum between the plates equation (1.30) will give the value of permittivity for free space usually denoted by ϵ_0.

If we suppose the condenser to be discharged through a ballistic galvanometer, of sensitivity k coulombs per division, giving a deflexion θ divisions, then $Q = k\theta$.

Substituting in (1.29)

$$\epsilon_0 = \frac{k\theta}{V} \cdot \frac{d}{a} \quad (1.31)$$

where all the quantities on the right-hand side are measurable. The value obtained from careful measurements is

$$\epsilon_0 = 8.85 \times 10^{-12} \text{ farads (metre)}^{-1}.$$

A more easily-remembered form is

$$\epsilon_0 = \frac{1}{36\pi} \times 10^{-9} \text{ m.k.s. units.}$$

In the c.g.s. system of units the force, equation (1.1), is defined by stating that a force of 1 dyne is produced between two charges, each of 1 statcoulomb, placed 1 cm apart in vacuum. Thus the value of permittivity, ϵ_0, for free space (vacuum), in the m.k.s. system, will also be given by substitution of the appropriate c.g.s./m.k.s. conversion factors, i.e.

$$\epsilon_0 = \frac{q_1 q_2}{4\pi F r^2} = \frac{(1/3 \times 10^{-9})^2}{4\pi . 10^{-5}(10^{-2})^2} = \frac{1}{36\pi} \times 10^{-9} \text{ farads/metre.}$$

We may align the two systems of units by introducing *relative permittivity* ϵ_r, defined by $\epsilon = \epsilon_r \epsilon_0$ farads/metre in which ϵ_r is a pure number and has the same value as the permittivity (or, more commonly, dielectric constant) on the c.g.s. scale. Thus a material having a dielectric constant of 2 in the c.g.s. system will have a relative permittivity of 2 and an absolute permittivity of

$$2 \times 8.854 \times 10^{-12} = 17.708 \times 10^{-12} \text{ farads/metre.}$$

In engineering it is common to describe a material by its relative permittivity, and the word relative is often dropped. There should never be any confusion, however, since absolute permittivity will always include a negative power of 10 whilst relative permittivity will generally be a number greater than unity.

Complex Permittivity

Permittivity, $\epsilon = \epsilon_r \epsilon_0$, has been defined as a property of the medium by means of Coulomb's law, where ϵ_r is the relative permittivity.

If a parallel-plate condenser has a capacitance C_0 in air, and the space between the plates is filled by a medium of permittivity ϵ_r then, neglecting fringing effects, the capacitance becomes $C = \epsilon_r C_0$.

When an alternating e.m.f., v, is applied across the condenser an alternating current, i, will flow, its value being

$$i = j\omega\epsilon_r C_0 v$$

provided that the dielectric is a 'perfect' one. In general, however, an in-phase component of current will appear corresponding to a resistive current between the condenser plates. Such current is entirely due to the dielectric medium and is a property of it. We therefore characterize it by a component of permittivity by defining relative permittivity as

$$\epsilon_r = \epsilon' - j\epsilon''.$$

The current in the condenser then becomes

$$i = j\omega(\epsilon' - j\epsilon'') C_0 v$$

or $$i = \omega\epsilon'' C_0 v + j\omega\epsilon' C_0 v \qquad (1.32)$$

and it has a real component. The magnitude of ϵ'' will be defined by the magnitude of the in-phase, or 'loss', component of the current. It will be noted that this mode of definition does not require us to say anything about the type of loss mechanism envisaged in the dielectric.

It is conventional to describe the performance of a condenser in terms of its loss angle, δ, which is the phase-angle between the total current, i, and the purely quadrature component i_C. If the in-phase component is i_L, then

$$|i| = (|i_L|^2 + |i_C|^2)^{1/2}$$

and $$\tan\delta = \frac{|i_L|}{|i_C|} = \frac{\omega\epsilon'' C_0 v}{\omega\epsilon' C_0 v} \quad \text{i.e.,} \quad \tan\delta = \frac{\epsilon''}{\epsilon'} \qquad (1.33)$$

(1.32) may be regarded as the definition of ϵ'' and, at the same time, indicates the basis of its measurement. When the dielectric medium is 'loss-free', ϵ'' will be zero.

It is sometimes convenient to use the concept of *dielectric conductivity*. The capacitance of an air-filled, parallel-plate condenser is given, neglecting fringing effects, by

$$C_0 = \frac{A}{d} \epsilon_0 \text{ farads}$$

where A is the area of the condenser, and d the distance between the plates. With an applied alternating e.m.f., v, and a dielectric between the plates, the current is given by

$$i = j\omega(\epsilon' - j\epsilon'')\frac{A}{d}\epsilon_0 v.$$

But the field strength, E, between the plates, is v/d V/m and the current density J is i/A A/m, therefore

$$J = j\omega\epsilon_0 \epsilon' E + \omega\epsilon_0 \epsilon'' E.$$

Now, by definition, conductivity (which may be complex) is the ratio J/E, and we have

$$\frac{J}{E} = j\omega\epsilon_0 \epsilon' + \omega\epsilon_0 \epsilon''.$$

In the dielectric, however, the imaginary term is already accounted for by the capacitance, which involves the real part, ϵ', of the relative permittivity. Thus we define dielectric conductivity as the real part of the ratio J/E in the above expression, i.e.,

$$\sigma_d = \omega\epsilon_0 \epsilon''. \tag{1.34}$$

Dielectric conductivity represents the sum of all the loss mechanisms in the material, and is a measure of the performance of a dielectric as an insulator.

Polarization

When connected to a battery an air condenser will charge until the free charges on each plate produce a potential difference equal and opposite to the battery voltage. A dielectric increases the charge-storage capacity of a condenser by neutralizing some of the free charges which would otherwise contribute to the p.d. opposing the battery voltage. More charge can, as a result, flow into the condenser which then has an increased storage capacity given by $\epsilon_r C_0$, where C_0 was the original capacity in air. We visualize this effect as arising from alignment of electrostatic dipoles in the dielectric under the influence of the field between the condenser plates. The dipoles form long chains with a positive charge at one end and a negative at the other. The positive charge will be adjacent to the negative condenser plate and will neutralize some of the charge on it. Similarly the negative end of the dipole chain will neutralize some of the charge on the positive condenser plate.

For an applied battery voltage, V, the charge carried by the air condenser will be $Q_0 = C_0 V$ and, on insertion of the dielectric, $Q = \epsilon_r C_0 V$.

Since we are not, in this argument, considering loss mechanisms, ϵ_r may be replaced by ϵ' (ϵ'' assumed zero) and we may write

$$\frac{Q}{\epsilon'} = C_0 V$$

or

$$V \propto \frac{Q}{\epsilon'}.$$

The implication is that, of the total charge Q, only a fraction Q/ϵ', contributes to neutralization of the applied voltage, the remainder $Q\{1 - (1/\epsilon')\}$ being bound charge neutralized by the polarization of the dielectric.

Now the total charge Q is distributed over the plates of the condenser and we may represent it as a surface charge q_a per unit area. By Gauss' law, for an infinitesimal area, dA, of the condenser plate

$$q_a . dA = \mathbf{D} . \mathbf{dS}$$

where $\mathbf{dS}$ will be the area of a surface (like a pillbox) enclosing dA. If there were no dielectric the charge

$$\frac{q_a}{\epsilon'} . dA = \mathbf{D}_a . \mathbf{dS} = \epsilon_0 \mathbf{E} . \mathbf{dS}. \tag{1.35}$$

We define a *polarization* vector $\mathbf{P}$ to account for the bound charge density $q_a\{1 - (1/\epsilon')\}$ such that

$$q_a \left(1 - \frac{1}{\epsilon'}\right) dA = \mathbf{P} . \mathbf{dS} \tag{1.36}$$

since

$$q_a = \frac{q_a}{\epsilon'} + q_a \left(1 - \frac{1}{\epsilon'}\right)$$

we have from (1.35) and (1.36)

$$q_a\, dA = \epsilon_0 \mathbf{E}.\mathbf{dS} + \mathbf{P}.\mathbf{dS} = \mathbf{D}.\mathbf{dS}$$

or in general,

$$\mathbf{D} = \epsilon_0 \mathbf{E} + \mathbf{P}. \tag{1.37}$$

But $\mathbf{D} = \epsilon' \epsilon_0 \mathbf{E}$ for the dielectric, so that

$$\mathbf{P} = \epsilon_0 (\epsilon' - 1) \mathbf{E} = \chi \epsilon_0 \mathbf{E} \tag{1.38}$$

where $\chi = (\epsilon' - 1)$ is called the *dielectric susceptibility* of the medium and is clearly given by

$$\frac{\text{(bound charge density)}}{\text{(free charge density)}}.$$

From (1.37) $\mathbf{P}$ will have the same dimensions as $\mathbf{D}$, i.e. coulomb (metre)$^{-2}$.

The polarization of a dielectric is the analogue of the magnetization of a magnetic material, and for a ferromagnetic we have a relation comparable to (1.38):

$$\mathbf{M} = \chi_m \mathbf{H}$$

where χ_m is the magnetic susceptibility and $\mathbf{M}$ the spontaneous magnetization of the material. In a similar way certain dielectric materials exhibit spontaneous polarization and are termed 'ferro-electric', by analogy with the ferromagnetic case. Materials with a small, positive magnetic susceptibility are termed paramagnetic and acquire a magnetization in an applied field, which disappears on removal of the field. Analogous dielectric materials, which exhibit a polarization in an electric field, are termed 'paraelectric'. Such materials will have a small positive electric susceptibility. In fact, all dielectrics are paraelectric with exception of vacuum, which has a susceptibility of precisely zero. There is no dielectric equivalent to the diamagnetic material which has a negative magnetic suscepti-bility.

The measurement of the polarization of a material is based on (1.38) and consists in measurement of χ or, in practice, of ϵ'. Methods of measurement are dealt with in the next chapter.

Depolarization

In the previous section it was assumed that the free ends of the dipole chains, produced by polarization of the dielectric, are neutralized by charges bound at the electrode surfaces. In this case the macroscopic electric field inside the dielectric is identical with the electric field measured outside it, i.e. by measurement of the voltage between the electrodes. In the absence of electrodes, however, there will be a closure field between the free charges at the ends of the dipole chains. This field will extend between the positive and negative ends of the dipole chains through the space outside the dielectric. It may be denoted by $\mathbf{E}_e$; the field inside the dielectric is $\mathbf{E}_i$ and will be smaller than $\mathbf{E}_e$ by an amount proportional to the polarization $\mathbf{P}$. The constant of proportionality is called the depolarizing factor, β, and depends on the geometry of the specimen, i.e.

$$\epsilon_0(\mathbf{E}_e - \mathbf{E}_i) = \beta\mathbf{P}. \tag{1.39}$$

The depolarization factor, β, as defined by (1.39) is identical with the demagnetization factor encountered in magnetism, and is calculated in the same way. Its calculation is a difficult matter, and can only be done exactly for relatively simple geometries. Tables of demagnetization factors have been listed[1] and a few simple cases can readily be remembered; for a sphere $\beta = 1/3$, for a long rod with $\mathbf{E}$ parallel to its length $\beta = 0$ and for a very short rod $\beta = 1$. In the case of a long rod with $\mathbf{E}$ perpendicular to its length $\beta = 1/2$.

CHAPTER 2

Measurement of Permittivity

Introduction

A wide variety of methods exist for the measurement of permittivity, the particular method adopted being determined by the nature of the specimen and the frequency range in which the measurement is made. In the following sections methods suitable for each frequency range will be described, and their application to solids, liquids and gases discussed.

The measurement of the real part of relative permittivity, ϵ', is generally done by measuring the change in capacitance of a condenser, brought about by the introduction of the dielectric between its electrodes. The imaginary part, ϵ'', is found from measurement of $\tan\delta$, the loss factor arising from the introduction of the dielectric. Accurate measurement demands care in the design of the measuring apparatus and types of measuring cell will be discussed.

D.C. Permittivity

A simple method for determining the d.c., or initial, relative permittivity is to measure the time-constant for discharge of a condenser, through a standard resistor, with and without the dielectric present.

The air-filled condenser, capacitance C_0, is assumed loss-free and is charged to a known voltage V_0 from a battery. At time $t = 0$ it is connected across a high resistance R and the voltage V_1 across R, at time t_1, is noted. This voltage may be measured by means of a high-impedance voltmeter connected across R, the value taken for R being that of the parallel combination of the resistance itself and the resistance of the voltmeter. If we write $t_1 - t = \tau_0$ then

$$\log\frac{V_0}{V_1} = \frac{\tau_0}{C_0 R}$$

from which C_0 is found. The dielectric is now inserted and the time τ for the voltage to fall to a convenient value V is found; then

$$\log \frac{V_0}{V} = \frac{\tau}{CR_p} \tag{2.1}$$

where C is the new capacitance of the condenser and R_p is the total shunt resistance in the circuit. The latter will include the effect of losses in the dielectric, which may be treated as a resistor R_L in parallel with C. Then

$$R_p = \frac{RR_L}{R+R_L}$$

and it is necessary to determine the value of R_p.

Since (2.1) contains two unknown quantities it is required to obtain a second equation. This may be done by connecting a standard air-capacitor, C_1, of negligible loss, in parallel with C, and noting the time τ_1 for the voltage to fall from V_0 to the same value V. Then we have

$$\frac{\tau}{CR_p} = \frac{\tau_1}{(C+C_1)R_p} \quad \text{whence C} = \frac{C_1}{\left(\dfrac{\tau_1}{\tau}-1\right)}. \tag{2.2}$$

and R_p may be found by substitution in (2.1).

The relation between R_p and ϵ'' is discussed further in Chapter 3. The value of ϵ' is simply C/C_0.

The applicability of this method is limited to cases for which the time-constant C_0R can be made long enough to permit observation. Where the C_0R product is of the order of milliseconds the discharge can be observed using a cathode-ray oscilloscope, with a long-persistence screen, connected across R in place of the voltmeter. With a slow sweep applied at the same moment as the condenser connexion is transferred from the source of e.m.f. to R, the discharge trace displayed on the screen will permit measurement of τ. The method can be used for discharge times as short as 1 millisecond, corresponding to a frequency of 100 c/s. Errors in the determination are associated with measurement of the voltage reached after a given time, and with the time measurement itself, through difficulty in knowing precisely the moment of commencement of the discharge.

An alternative method has been devised by Cole and Cole[2], in which the charging current of the condenser containing the dielectric is observed. The current decreases from its initial value to a value corresponding to the leakage current in a manner determined by the polarization of the dielectric. The current-time curve can be related to the complex permittivity of the dielectric by means of fitting it to standard curves, given in Cole's paper. The theory involved is based upon relaxation processes dealt with in Chapter 6. The condenser is placed in series with a charging resistance chosen to give a reasonable time-constant. A convenient method of current measurement is by means of a d.c. voltage amplifier connected across the resistance, a graph of its output voltage against time being the required current-time graph. The leakage current, which must be determined separately, is the value of current flowing after a time long compared with the time-constant of the circuit. The capacitance, C_0 of the air-filled condenser is also required to be known.

The accuracy of the method depends again on the accuracy of current and time measurement, but is capable of being slightly better than that of the first method described.

Bridge Measurements

For frequencies in the audio to high range (10^2 to 10^7 c/s) one of the many a.c. bridges may be used for the measurement of permittivity.

Of these the Schering bridge, shown in Fig. 4, is most usually used since it is suitable for higher frequencies and can be calibrated for direct reading of $\tan \delta$.

Referring to Fig. 4, C represents the dielectric-filled condenser and R the dielectric loss. C_2 and C_3 are standard, calibrated condensers and the resistors R_1 and R_2 are usually made equal. C_1 represents stray capacity across R_1 and will, for the moment, be neglected.

Initially, without the dielectric present,

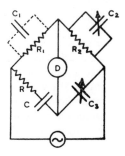

Fig. 4. Schering bridge

$C = C_0$, $R = 0$ and if $R_1 = R_2$, the balance equations are

$$C_0 = C_3$$

and
$$C_2 = 0. \tag{2.3}$$

With the dielectric inserted, the equations become

$$C = C_3$$

and
$$R = \frac{R_1 C_2}{C_3}. \tag{2.4}$$

Since $\tan \delta = \omega CR$, it will be seen that

$$\tan \delta = \omega C_2 R_2 = \frac{1}{\tan \delta_2}. \tag{2.5}$$

Thus C_2 may be calibrated directly in terms of $\tan \delta$.

From the definition of complex permittivity $\epsilon''/\epsilon' = \tan \delta$ and $\epsilon' = C/C_0$ so that (2.3) and (2.4) yield the permittivity values at the chosen frequency.

If the stray capacity C_1 is not negligible, as is usually the case in practice, the balance equations become

$$C = \frac{C_3 R_2}{R_1(1 + \omega^2 C_1 C_3 R_2 R)} \tag{2.6}$$

and
$$R = R_1 \frac{C_2}{C_3} - \frac{C_1}{C}.$$

There are now cross-terms present having the implication (if C_1 is neglected) that the values calculated for C and R are in error. This is particularly true if the dielectric losses, and therefore R, are large, since the product $C_1 R$ then becomes large. This may be illustrated by a numerical example.

Take a dielectric having a relative permittivity $5 - j0 \cdot 5$; the value of $\tan \delta$ is $0 \cdot 1$ which corresponds to a fairly high loss. Assume the specimen-holder to have an air-capacity, C_0, of 200 pF and the measurement to be made at $\omega = 10^8$. The equivalent series resistor is given by (see equation 3.6)

$$R_s = \frac{R_p}{1 + (\omega C_p R_p)^2}$$

and the equivalent series capacitance is given by (see equation 3.2)

$$C_s = \frac{1}{\omega^2 C_p R_s R_p}.$$

Now by equation (1.32) $R_p = 1/\omega\epsilon'' C_0$ and $C_p = \epsilon' C_0$ thus, using the above figures, $R_p = 100\ \Omega$ and $C_p = 1000$ pF, which give $R_s = 0.99\ \Omega$ and $C_s = 1010$ pF. If these figures are substituted in the equation (2.6), which allow for the stray capacitance C_1, and we take the value of the latter to be 10 pF, we may calculate the 'dial settings', i.e. the values of C_3 and C_2, for balance, assuming $R_1 = R_2 = 100\ \Omega$. The results of these calculations are $C_3 = 1020$ pF and $C_2 = 22.2$ pF. Now if these dial readings were used in the un-corrected balance, equations (2.4), the apparent values would be $C_{s(app)} = 1020$ pF and $R_{s(app)} = 1.98\ \Omega$, the errors being 1.0% in C_s and 50% in R_s.

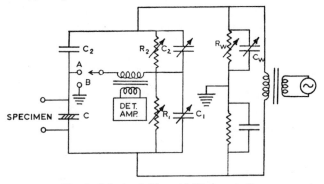

Fig. 5. Schering bridge with Wagner earth

Since it is extremely difficult to ensure that there shall be no stray capacity present across R, it is usual to connect a standard capacitor as C_1 with a value (say 100 pF) sufficient to swamp the stray capacitance. Error from this source is then much reduced and the bridge can be used for measurements on high-loss materials.

To avoid other inaccuracies arising from stray capacitance to earth, it is usual to incorporate the Wagner earth, as illustrated in Fig. 5, which shows a full, practical bridge circuit. The object of the

Wagner earth is to adjust the potential at the junction of C_3 and the specimen to earth potential without physically connecting it to earth. This avoids earth currents, which would arise in an actual connexion, but at the same time makes the bridge symmetrical to earth, with consequent balancing of stray capacitances.

With the switch in position A the bridge is balanced roughly; the switch is then transferred to B and the Wagner earth condenser C_ω and resistor R_ω are adjusted for balance. The bridge is alternately switched from A to B and back until a sharp balance is achieved. Careful attention must, of course, be paid to screening and the avoidance of hand capacity and stray pick-up effects. If this is done such a bridge may be worked up to as high as 100 Mc/s in favourable circumstances.

Measuring Cells

In all the foregoing methods accuracy depends critically on the measuring cell in which the specimen is mounted. Since it is necessary to be able to calculate the air capacity of the system from its geometry, the construction must necessarily be simple. The usual arrangement, for solids, comprises flat, parallel plates, of known area and separation, between which is inserted the specimen, in the form of a parallel-sided disc of diameter slightly less than that of the condenser plates.

Errors in this arrangement are associated with the inductance and resistance of the leads to the electrodes, stray capacitance from these leads to earth and fringe fields at the edges of the electrodes. Hartshorn and Ward[3] developed a two-terminal measuring cell comprising a fixed base electrode at earth potential and an upper electrode, parallel to it, driven by a micrometer screw. In use, the bridge is balanced with the specimen in place initially. The specimen is then removed and the micrometer electrode screwed in until the bridge is restored to balance. The change in capacitance, due to insertion of the specimen, is determined by noting the amount by which the electrode is moved, the cell having been calibrated separately. By this method the inductance, resistance and stray capacitance of the leads and the edge capacitance are maintained practically constant and their effects virtually eliminated.

The same type of cell may be used for measurements on liquids if a ring of low-loss material, such as P.T.F.E., is clamped between the electrodes to contain the liquid.

Von Hippel[4] has given a full discussion of types of cell and corrections necessary, and quotes an ultimate possible accuracy of approximately 0.2% in the measurement of capacitance and 2% in the measurement of $\tan\delta$.

Resonant Circuit Methods

For frequencies in the range 10 Mc/s to 100 Mc/s bridge methods are generally difficult due to the increasing importance of the effects of stray capacitance. It is usual to make the measurements by use of a resonant circuit of which the whole or part of the capacitance is the

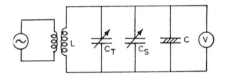

Fig. 6. Circuit for resonance method

dielectric measuring cell. The micrometer electrode system is invariably used; the circuit is brought to resonance initially by means of a tuning capacitor in parallel with the measuring cell, and, after removal of the dielectric, the circuit is restored to resonance by adjustment of the micrometer electrode. This provides relatively easy and accurate measurement of the real part of permittivity, providing the losses are sufficiently small for the circuit to retain a reasonably adequate Q factor, i.e. that the resonance peak remains sharp enough for accurate adjustment. The measurement of the loss factor is most easily done by measurement of the resonance curve width at 3 dB down, i.e. at the points where the voltage across the condenser has fallen to $1/\sqrt{2}$ of its value at resonance.

Referring to Fig. 6, the micrometer electrode system, C, is connected in series with a coil L which is coupled to the signal source. Initial tuning is accomplished by varying the tuning capacitor, C_T, until a maximum reading is obtained on the vacuum-tube voltmeter

V. With the dielectric in place the resonance curve width is found by
varying the small trimmer capacitor, C_s, until the voltmeter reads
$1/\sqrt{2}$ of its peak value on either side of resonance. The change δC_s,
in C_s, is then a measure of the bandwidth. In the Hartshorn-Ward
design this capacitor is built into the test cell.

The circuit arrangement is shown in Fig. 6: little error is involved
in treating this as a series LCR circuit, where the series resistance R
represents the sum of coil resistance and dielectric loss, whilst the
capacitance is the sum of C_T, C_s, and C. For the series resonant
circuit the bandwidth, $2\delta\omega$, at 3 dB down is related to the Q factor by

$$Q = \frac{\omega_0}{2\delta\omega} = \frac{\omega_0 L}{R} = \frac{1}{\omega_0 CR}$$

where C is the total capacity and R the total resistance.

The bandwidth is measured, by the method described above, with
the dielectric in place, and with it removed. If the detuning is ΔC_s in
the first case and $\Delta C_s'$ in the second case the value of the dielectric
loss resistance may be extracted. For a series LCR circuit

$$\omega_0 = \frac{1}{LC}$$

$$\frac{\partial \omega_0}{\omega_0} = -\frac{\partial C}{2C}.$$

Thus

$$\frac{1}{Q} = \frac{2\delta\omega}{\omega_0} = \frac{\Delta C_s}{C_{\text{total}}} = \omega_0 C_{\text{total}}(R_d + R_1) \qquad (2.7)$$

where R_d is the dielectric loss resistance, and R_1 the coil resistance,
and $C_{\text{total}} = C_T + C_S + C$. Similarly

$$\frac{1}{Q'} = 2\frac{\partial \omega'}{\omega_0} = \frac{\Delta C_S'}{C_{\text{total}}} = \omega_0 C_{\text{total}} R_L \qquad (2.8)$$

remembering that, after removal of the dielectric from the cell, the
micrometer electrodes are readjusted to the same capacitance C.

Combining (2.7) and (2.8) we have

$$R_d = \frac{\Delta C_S - \Delta C_S'}{2\omega_0 C_{\text{total}}^2} \qquad (2.9)$$

whence ϵ'' may be calculated by

$$\epsilon'' \doteqdot \omega_0 C_0 R_d (\epsilon')^2 \qquad (2.10)$$

C_0 is calculated in the usual manner, from the measuring cell geometry and ϵ' from C/C_0.

Because there is an irreducible minimum capacitance represented by the measurement cell, the higher frequencies must be reached by reducing the inductance of the coil. This worsens the Q factor so that, for frequencies in excess of 100 Mc/s, accurate measurement becomes impossible.

Double Resonance Method

The measurements described in the foregoing section are limited to relatively low-loss materials ($\tan \delta \sim 0.05$ approx.). For the cases where $\tan \delta$ is higher the damping of the tuned circuit is so great that the resonance frequency cannot be accurately determined. Since many doped semiconductor materials have loss factors of 0.1 or more, and since considerable theoretical interest centres on the behaviour of their permittivities with frequency, it is necessary to have an alternative method for measurement of ϵ' in the presence of high losses.

In the double-resonance method the cell containing the specimen forms the capacitance of a second resonant circuit which is coupled to a first resonant circuit energized by a signal generator. The principle of the method is that, with the resonant circuit containing the high-loss specimen coupled by a small condenser to the first resonant circuit, the resonance of the latter is sharper than that of the circuit containing the specimen. The method has been described by Ichijo[5], who used the circuit shown in Fig. 7.

When the first circuit is tuned to resonance the second is adjusted for minimum value of current through the detector, by means of C_s. It can be shown that the condition for minimum value of this current is independent of the resistance present in the second circuit, thus the capacitance introduced by the dielectric, and hence the real part of permittivity, can be determined independently of the losses in the dielectric.

The experimental method is first to short out the second circuit by means of S_3 and to tune the first to resonance, as indicated by maximum detector current, by means of C_n. S_3 is then opened and, with the specimen in place, C_S is adjusted for minimum detector current.

The dielectric is then removed and C_S again adjusted for minimum current. The difference between the two readings of C_S is then the value of the capacitance introduced by the dielectric.

The equivalent loss resistance, R_x, is determined in a similar way. To evaluate it, however, it is necessary also to determine R_0, the loss of the second resonant circuit. The first resonant circuit is tuned to

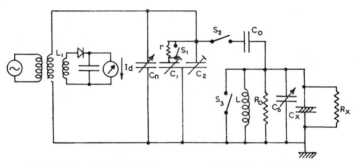

Fig. 7. Circuit for double-resonance method (after Ichijo[5])

resonance, with S_1 closed shorting out r, by means of C_n. S_3 is then opened, the specimen removed and C_S adjusted for minimum detector current as before, this value of current being noted. S_3 is then closed and, with S_1 open, C_1 and r are adjusted to bring the detector current back to the noted value.

If the value of the differential condenser is then C_{10} and of the resistance is r, Ichijo shows that

$$R_0 = \frac{C_{10} r_1^2}{C_0^2} \tag{2.11}$$

where R_0 is the total loss resistance of the second resonant circuit and C_0 the value of the coupling capacitance. The specimen is then inserted and the procedure repeated to give the total loss resistance

$$R_r = \frac{C_{11}^2 r_2}{C_0^2}. \qquad (2.12)$$

For the (usual) case of $R_0 \gg R_x$ we may take $R_x = R_r$. Tan δ is given by

$$\tan \delta = \frac{1}{\omega C_x R_x}. \qquad (2.13)$$

Ichijo quotes measurements on materials with $\tan \delta$ in the region of unity and real part of permittivity up to 21, at frequencies up to 10 Mc/s.

Transmission-line Measurements

In the V.H.F. range, 100—1000 Mc/s, the tuned-circuit technique cannot be employed due to the impossibility of realizing a lumped

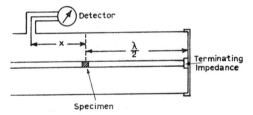

Fig. 8. Circuit for standing wave measurement of permittivity of dielectric disc

resonant circuit at these frequencies. Distributed circuits must be used, the common forms of which are transmission-lines and wave-guides. The latter are inconveniently bulky in the V.H.F. range, and transmission line methods are generally employed for the measurement of permittivity.

A variety of methods exists, based on travelling-wave and standing-wave measurements. In the one most usually used for solids the specimen represents a terminating impedance for a coaxial transmission line, causing standing-waves to be set up. By measurement of the positions and magnitudes of the maxima and minima, with a probe-type standing-wave detector, the permittivity of the specimen may be determined.

In the arrangement of Fig. 8 the specimen is in the form of a thin disc of the same diameter as the inner conductor of a coaxial line. A half-wavelength beyond the disc the line is terminated. A probe-type detector can be moved along the length of the line to determine the positions and magnitudes of the maxima and minima of the standing-wave pattern.

With the line initially short-circuited at the receiving end a short circuit is transformed to the plane of the specimen by the $\lambda/2$ length of line. We may regard the line as terminated at this plane in an impedance $Z = R + jX$, due to the specimen.

Treating the line as loss-free, with a characteristic impedance Z_0 and propagation constant $\beta = 2\pi/\lambda$, the voltage V_x at a distance x from the specimen is given by

$$V_x = \frac{V_0 e^{-j\beta}}{2} (e^{j\beta x} + u e^{-j\beta x}) \qquad (2.14)$$

where V_0 is the input voltage to the line and u is the reflection coefficient due to the terminating impedance Z and is given by

$$u = \frac{Z - Z_0}{Z + Z_0}. \qquad (2.15)$$

Equation (2.14) assumes that the generator is perfectly matched to the line so that there are no reflections at the generator end.

Substituting for u in equation (2.14) and expanding the exponential terms we have

$$V_x = \frac{V_0 e^{-j\beta}}{Z + Z_0} \{R\cos\beta x + j(X\cos\beta x + Z_0 \sin\beta x)\}$$

from which the modulus is

$$|V_x| = \frac{V_0}{|Z + Z_0|} \{R^2\cos^2\beta x + (X\cos\beta x + Z_0\sin\beta x)^2\}^{1/2}.$$

If we assume a square-law detector to be used so that its output voltage is given by $E = A|V|^2$, where A is a constant, then

$$E_x = \frac{AV_0^2}{|Z+Z_0|^2}\{(R^2+X^2)\cos^2\beta x + Z_0^2\sin^2\beta x + 2XZ_0\sin\beta x\cos\beta x\}.$$

At a distance of half a wavelength from the specimen the voltage will be a minimum if $Z < Z_0$: then $\beta x = \pi$ and the equation reduces to

$$E_{x1} = \frac{AV_0^2}{|Z+Z_0|^2}(R^2+X^2). \tag{2.16}$$

At a quarter-wavelength from the specimen we have a voltage maximum with $\beta x = \pi/2$ and

$$E_{x2} = \frac{AV_0^2}{|Z+Z_0|^2}Z_0^2 \tag{2.17}$$

taking the ratio

$$\frac{Ex_1}{Ex_2} = \frac{R^2+X^2}{Z_0^2}. \tag{2.18}$$

The positions of minimum and maximum voltage will be interchanged if $Z > Z_0$.

If, now, we terminate the line with its characteristic impedance, instead of with a short circuit, the above calculation still applies, but with a terminating impedance $Z + Z_0$. Then

$$\frac{Ex_1'}{Ex_2'} = \frac{(R+Z_0)^2+X^2}{Z_0^2} \tag{2.19}$$

subtracting

$$\frac{Ex_1'}{Ex_2'} - \frac{Ex_1}{Ex_2} = \frac{2R}{Z_0}+1. \tag{2.20}$$

Since Z_0 is known and the left-hand side of the equation represents the measured quantities, R is determined: substitution in equation (2.18) then gives X.

Neglecting fringing fields, the capacitance of the specimen will be given by $C = \epsilon' \epsilon_0 a/d$ where a is the area of the disc and d its thickness.

Now

$$X = -\frac{1}{\omega C} = -\frac{d}{\omega\epsilon'\epsilon_0 a}$$

hence

$$\epsilon' = -\frac{d}{\omega X\epsilon_0 a} = \frac{1}{\omega C_0 X}. \tag{2.21}$$

(Note: in the evaluation of X from equation (2.18) the negative sign should be taken for the square-root.)

The dielectric conductivity of the material is $\sigma_d = \omega\epsilon''\epsilon_0$ (equation 1.34) so that it will have a resistance $R_p = d/\sigma_d a$ effectively in parallel with X. Since the resistance R, evaluated in the experiment, is a series element we transform it to an equivalent parallel resistance by $R_p = X^2/R$. Combining these we obtain

$$\epsilon'' = \frac{\omega\epsilon'\epsilon_0 aR}{d} = \omega(\epsilon')^2 RC_0. \tag{2.22}$$

This method has been used by Fatuzzo[6] for the evaluation of small changes in the permittivity of ferroelectrics during switching.

For measurements on liquids and gases the transmission line may be filled with the medium being measured. The permittivity may be deduced from measurement of the propagation constant of the line.

Microwave Measurements

In the frequency range above 100 Mc/s it becomes desirable to use waveguide or cavity resonator techniques. The particular mode of measurement employed depends upon the nature and quantity of material to be measured.

Considering solids, if a sufficient quantity of the material is available, the simplest method to treat theoretically is that in which the whole cross-section of the waveguide may be filled with the material. The full theory has been given by Lurio and Stern[7] for the case of a block of material, with plane faces perpendicular to the direction of propagation, completely filling the guide. When the specimen is of length such that it corresponds precisely to a number of half-wavelengths, at the frequency used, in the dielectric medium of permittivity ϵ', the power transmitted through it is a maximum. For a given length of specimen, if the frequency is gradually increased, the transmitted power will go through a succession of maxima. If the frequency separation between the maxima is Δf, if is easy to show that

$$(\epsilon') = \frac{c}{2d\Delta f} \tag{2.23}$$

where d is the length of the specimen and c the velocity of light. The fraction, T, of the incident power which is transmitted by the dielectric is given by

$$\frac{1}{T} = 1 + \frac{\epsilon'}{4\left\{1 - \left(\frac{\lambda_0}{\lambda_c}\right)^2\right\}\cos\delta} \cdot \sinh^2\frac{(2d\pi X)}{\lambda_0} + \sin^2\frac{(2d\pi U)}{\lambda_0}$$

$$+ \frac{1}{2\left\{1 - \left(\frac{\lambda_0}{\lambda_c}\right)^2\right\}^{1/2}} \cdot U\sinh\frac{4d\pi X}{\lambda_0} + X\sin\frac{4d\pi U}{\lambda_0}, \tag{2.24}$$

where $U = \dfrac{\{\epsilon'(1+\cos\delta)\}^{1/2}}{2\cos\delta}, \quad X = \dfrac{\{\epsilon'(1-\cos\delta)\}^{1/2}}{2\cos\delta},$

$\tan\delta = \epsilon''/\epsilon'$, λ_0 is the free space wavelength and λ_c the cut-off wavelength of the guide. From this $\tan\delta$ can be calculated.

Where only a small quantity of the material is available, it is more convenient to use a resonant cavity method of measurement. It can be shown that if a resonant cavity is 'perturbed' by the introduction of a small dielectric specimen its resonant frequency is lowered. The shift in frequency is directly related to the ϵ' of the specimen, whilst the change in the cavity's Q factor is directly related to ϵ'' for the material.

In a cylindrical cavity, excited in the fundamental mode E_{010}, the E-field is a maximum along the central axis of the cavity. The dielectric specimen is placed in this region, producing a maximum effect. It can be shown, for a small specimen (see, for instance, Horner et al.[8]), that

$$\epsilon' = 1 - 0.539\frac{V_0}{V}\frac{\Delta f}{f_0} \tag{2.25}$$

where V_0 is the cavity and V the specimen volume, and f_0 is the original resonant frequency. (Note: Δf will always be negative.) Also

$$\epsilon'' = 0.269 \frac{V_0}{V}\left(\frac{1}{Q} - \frac{1}{Q'}\right) \tag{2.26}$$

where Q is the magnification factor of the cavity with the specimen present. Q' is the magnification factor of the cavity with the specimen replaced by a supposed loss-free specimen of the same permittivity and dimensions. In practice Q' must be estimated: its theoretical value is

$$Q' = \frac{al}{(a+l)t} \tag{2.27}$$

where l is the axial length of the cavity, t the depth of current penetration in the cavity walls and a a radius of the cavity. In practice t is greater than that calculated from the skin-effect equations; the method adopted is to measure the Q of the air-filled cavity, by measuring the 3 dB width of the resonance curve, and to use it as Q' in equation (2.27), calculating a value for t. This value of t is then used, with a suitable correction for the lower frequency, in calculating Q' at the frequency of measurement.

This theory is based on a small perturbation, which means that the specimen to cavity radius should be in the region of 1/20 or less. For very low loss materials such a specimen volume means that it becomes very difficult to obtain an accurate value for ϵ''. In such cases the full treatment given by Horner et al. must be used.

The development of the perturbation equation is based on the idea of the field, in the vicinity of the specimen, being the same with and without it present. This is fulfilled, for a sufficiently small rod, when the rod stretches from top to bottom of the cavity. When a short rod is used correction must be made for the depolarizing field. The corrected value, ϵ', of permittivity will be given by

$$(\epsilon' - 1) = \frac{(\epsilon^* - 1)}{1 - A(\epsilon^* - 1)} \tag{2.28}$$

where ϵ^* is the measured value of ϵ' and A is the depolarizing factor for the specimen. Values for A are given by Bozorth[9].

The author has made cavity measurements with the modification of using an E_{020} cavity rather than E_{010}. This has two electrical and two magnetic nodes in the radius, the E-field again being a maximum at the centre where the specimen is placed. At the radius of the second

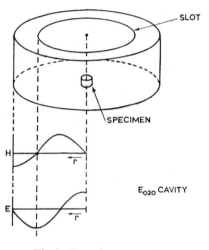

Fig. 9. E_{020} microwave cavity

magnetic node a slot may be cut in the cavity wall, as illustrated in Fig. 9, this being non-radiating and causing negligible disturbance of the cavity fields. In this way a readily removable plug can be made for opening the cavity to insert the specimen.

Advantage also derives from the fact that the coefficients of frequency shift and change in Q factor are smaller than in the E_{010} case, so that a given permittivity produces bigger changes in f and Q.

The appropriate formulae are obtained from the perturbation calculation for the E_{010} case with the difference that the argument of the Bessel function $J_0(Ka)$ for which J_0 is zero will be the second-order one, i.e. $5 \cdot 52$, instead of $2 \cdot 405$. This leads to

$$\epsilon' = 1 - 0 \cdot 23 \frac{V_0}{V} \frac{\Delta f}{f_0} \tag{2.29}$$

and

$$\epsilon'' = 0 \cdot 115 \frac{V_0}{V} \left(\frac{1}{Q} - \frac{1}{Q_u} \right). \tag{2.30}$$

There are many other methods for measuring permittivity at microwave frequencies. Details of the more important techniques have been given by Barlow and Cullen[10] who also include a bibliography of references to appropriate papers.

CHAPTER 3

Equivalent Circuits

Introduction

In Chapter 1 complex permittivity was introduced as a means of providing a parameter by which losses in a dielectric could be measured. The current through a dielectric-filled condenser, when an alternating e.m.f., v, was applied to it, was given by equation (1.32) as

$$i = \omega\epsilon'' C_0 v + j\omega\epsilon' C_0 v.$$

This implies that the condenser can be treated as pure, lossless capacitor, of reactance $1/\omega\epsilon' C_0$ in parallel with a resistor, R_p, of value $1/\omega\epsilon'' C_0$.

It is sometimes more convenient to treat the losses as a resistor, R_s, in series with the pure capacitance. The value of R_s equivalent to a given value of R_p is found by equating the impedances of the two circuits formed by C_p in parallel with R_p and by C_s in series with R_s. Thus

$$\frac{1 + j\omega C_s R_s}{j\omega C_s} = \frac{R_p}{1 + j\omega C_p R_p}. \tag{3.1}$$

Equating real parts gives

$$\frac{1}{\omega C_s R_s} = \omega C_p R_p \tag{3.2}$$

and imaginary parts give

$$\omega C_s R_s + \omega C_p R_p = \omega C_s R_p. \tag{3.3}$$

Using (3.2) in (3.3) we have

$$R_p = \frac{1 + \omega^2 C_s^2 R_s^2}{\omega^2 C_s^2 R_s}. \tag{3.4}$$

4

Now, for the series circuit, $\tan\delta = \omega C_s R_s$, and $\tan^2\delta \ll 1$ normally, so that

$$R_p \doteq \frac{X_s^2}{R_s}. \tag{3.5}$$

Similarly

$$\frac{1 + (\omega C_p R_p)^2}{\omega C_p R_p} = \frac{1}{\omega C_p R_s} \tag{3.6}$$

and since for the parallel circuit $\tan\delta = 1/\omega C_p R_p$, then $(\omega C_p R_p)^2 \gg 1$, therefore

$$R_s \doteq \frac{X_p^2}{R_p}. \tag{3.7}$$

Thus the dielectric loss can be represented by series or by parallel resistance, transformation from one to the other being readily effected by use of equations (3.5) and (3.7). It should be remembered, however, that ϵ'' is defined in terms of parallel resistance.

Frequency Variation of Permittivity

We have defined ϵ'' in terms of an equivalent resistor R_p, which accounts for the dielectric loss, whose value is $1/\omega\epsilon'' C_0$. Now, neglecting skin effect considerations, the value of a resistor must remain constant as a function of frequency. Thus the definition implies an inverse frequency variation for ϵ'', i.e.

$$\epsilon'' = \frac{1}{\omega R_p C_0} \propto \frac{1}{f}$$

where R_p is a constant. It was pointed out that the method of defining ϵ'' in terms of the in-phase component of current did not require any assumptions about the loss mechanism in the dielectric. This is only true if we are considering a fixed frequency since, as the above considerations show, a specific variation of ϵ'' with frequency is implied and this, in turn, confines the loss mechanism to one which could produce this particular frequency variation.

In practice both ϵ' and ϵ'' may vary with frequency, depending on the type of dielectric polarization involved. Thus an equivalent circuit representing the dielectric behaviour over a range of frequencies will often not be a simple two-element CR circuit.

When the permittivity varies markedly with frequency, the mechanism responsible for the variation can be characterized as a 'relaxation' or as a 'resonance'. The molecular nature of these mechanisms will be dealt with in a later chapter. A relaxation spectrum is generally characterized by a region of constant value followed by a slow fall of ϵ' to a low value as the frequency increases, the corresponding variation of ϵ'' being a broad peak. A resonance spectrum shows a rapid fall, from constant value, for ϵ' and a sharp peak in ϵ''.

Relaxation Spectra

These can always be represented by an equivalent circuit made up of resistive and capacitive elements only. The aim is to construct a network whose frequency response will be such as to correspond to the variations of ϵ' and ϵ'' with frequency found by experiment. Clearly there will be no unique solution, the equivalence between the dielectric-filled condenser and the circuit is purely formal and there will be a variety of possible circuits.

It has been pointed out that the parallel RC circuit implies a fall in ϵ'' with increasing frequency, according to $\epsilon'' \propto 1/f$. ϵ' is given by $C_p C_0$, where C_p is the capacitance of the dielectric-filled condenser, and is constant with frequency. Considering the series circuit, and using equation (3.4) we have:

$$R_p = \frac{1}{\omega \epsilon'' C_0} = \frac{1 + \omega^2 C_s^2 R_s^2}{\omega^2 C_s^2 R_s},$$

i.e.
$$\epsilon'' = \frac{\omega C_s^2 R_s}{C_0 \{1 + (\omega C_s R_s)^2\}}. \qquad (3.8)$$

From (3.2)

$$R_p = \frac{1}{\omega^2 C_s C_p R_s}.$$

Substituting for R_p and C_p

$$\frac{1}{\omega \epsilon'' C_0} = \frac{\epsilon''}{\omega^2 C_s \epsilon' C_0 R_s},$$

i.e.

$$\epsilon' = \frac{\epsilon''}{\omega C_s R_s}$$

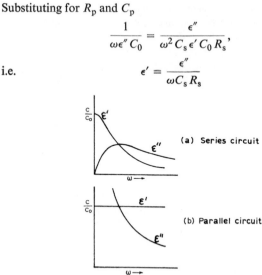

Fig. 10. Frequency dependence of permittivity assuming two simple equivalent circuits

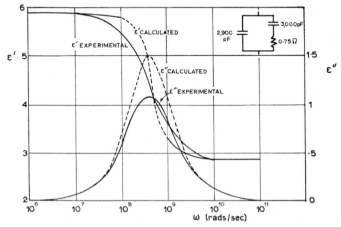

Fig. 11. Relaxation spectrum of 'Aroclor' transformer oil compared with spectrum for equivalent circuit shown

and using (3.8) we have

$$\epsilon' = \frac{C_s}{C_0\{1 + (\omega C_s R_s)^2\}}. \tag{3.9}$$

Equations (3.8) and (3.9) are plotted, as functions of frequency, in Fig. 10. It will be seen that ϵ'' goes through a broad maximum, whilst ϵ' falls, as frequency increases. Also shown are the variations of ϵ'' for the parallel circuit. A typical relaxation spectrum, for 'Aroclor' dielectric oil, is shown in Fig. 11. It will readily be seen that if the variations of the series circuit can be combined with the behaviour of the parallel circuit, almost any relaxation spectrum may be built up. We will consider the simplest series-parallel arrangement, shown in Fig. 12.

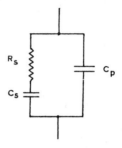

The admittance is given by

$$Y = \left(j\omega C_p + \frac{1}{Z_s}\right) \tag{3.10}$$

Fig. 12. Equivalent circuit of dielectric showing relaxation

where $Z_s = R_s + 1/j\omega C_s$. Now the time-constant of the series networks, assuming discharge with C_p shorted, is given by $C_s R_s = \tau_s$. Introducing this we have

$$Y = \frac{\omega^2 C_s \tau_s}{1 + \omega^2 \tau_s^2} + j\omega C_p + \frac{j\omega C_s}{1 + \omega^2 \tau_s^2}. \tag{3.11}$$

By definition, a capacitor containing a dielectric of relative permittivity $\epsilon_r = \epsilon' - j\epsilon''$, has an admittance

$$Y_c = j(\epsilon' - j\epsilon'')\omega C_0.$$

Equating Y and Y_c

$$\epsilon'' = \frac{C_s}{C_0} \cdot \frac{\omega \tau_s}{(1 + \omega^2 \tau_s^2)} \tag{3.12}$$

and

$$\epsilon' = \frac{C_p}{C_0} + \frac{C_s}{C_0} \cdot \frac{1}{1 + \omega^2 \tau_s^2} \tag{3.13}$$

and
$$\tan \delta = \frac{\epsilon''}{\epsilon'} = \frac{\omega \tau_s}{1 + \dfrac{C_p}{C_s}(1 + \omega^2 \tau_s^2)}. \tag{3.14}$$

These expressions may be used to fit the proposed circuit to a given relaxation spectrum by making use of the following expressions.

At zero frequency $\epsilon'' = 0$ and ϵ' has a maximum value since

$$\frac{\partial \epsilon'}{\partial \omega} = -\frac{C_s}{C_0} \cdot \frac{2\omega \tau_s^2}{(1 + \omega^2 \tau_s^2)^2}$$

which is zero for $\omega = 0$. This maximum value will be

$$\epsilon'_{\max} = \frac{C_p}{C_0} + \frac{C_s}{C_0} = \epsilon_s \tag{3.15}$$

and as frequency tends to infinity ϵ'' tends to zero and ϵ' tends to a minimum value

$$\epsilon'_{\min} = \frac{C_p}{C_0} = \epsilon_\infty. \tag{3.16}$$

The frequency at which the maximum value of ϵ'' occurs is given by

$$\frac{\partial \epsilon''}{\partial \omega} = 0 = C_0(1 + \omega^2 \tau_s^2) C_s \tau_s - C_s \omega \tau_s . 2\omega \tau_s^2 C_0$$

from which

$$\omega_{\max} = \frac{1}{\tau_s} = \frac{1}{C_s R_s} \tag{3.17}$$

and the maximum value of ϵ'' is

$$\epsilon''_{\max} = \frac{C_s}{2C_0}. \tag{3.18}$$

The frequency at which $\tan \delta$ is a maximum is given by

$$\frac{\partial \tan \delta}{\partial \omega} = 0 = C_s R_s \left(1 + \frac{C_p}{C_s}(1 + \omega^2 \tau_s^2)\right) - \omega \tau_s . \frac{C_p}{C_s} . 2\omega \tau_s^2$$

from which

$$\omega^2 = \frac{1 + C_s/C_p}{\tau_s^2} \qquad (3.19)$$

and the maximum value of $\tan \delta$ is

$$(\tan \delta)_{max} = \frac{(1 + C_s/C_p)^{1/2}}{2(1 + C_p/C_s)}. \qquad (3.20)$$

Equations (3.15) to (3.20) allow the values of C_p, C_s and R_s to be calculated, for a given dielectric, when the frequency spectrum of permittivity has been obtained. It should be noted, however, that it is necessary to know the value C_0, of the capacitance of the condenser before the introduction of dielectric, before explicit values C_p, C_s and R_s can be obtained. If this is not known, the values can only be given in terms of C_0.

As an example, we may attempt to derive the values for a circuit equivalent to the spectra for 'Aroclor' transformer oil given in Fig. 11. From the graphs we obtain $\epsilon_s = 5 \cdot 9$ and $\epsilon_\infty = 2 \cdot 9$. If we assume an arbitrary value of 1000 pF for C_0, we have, from (3.15) and (3.16), $C_p = 2900$ pF and $C_s = 3000$ pF. The angular frequency at which ϵ'' is a maximum is $4 \cdot 4 \times 10^8$ rads/sec and, using (3.17) we get $R_s = 0 \cdot 75 \Omega$. Substituting these values in (3.12) and (3.13) gives the spectra shown dotted in Fig. 11.

It will be seen that the fit between calculated and measured values is not very close; for example, the calculated ϵ'' max is $1 \cdot 5$ as against the experimental figure of $1 \cdot 1$. This is a very common result and has been discussed, in terms of mechanisms of polarization, by Cole and Cole whose work is described in Chapter 6.

In general this sort of disagreement is due to there being a spread of relaxation times about a mean value given by (3.17). The greater this spread the poorer will be the agreement between the calculated and measured curves. Accurate representation of the experimental results requires a more complicated equivalent circuit in which R_s is replaced by a complex impedance which is a function of frequency. Thus an accurate equivalent circuit for the dielectric is only possible, with fixed components, at a single frequency in the region near the relaxation frequency. Far removed from this region the equivalent circuit calculated on the basis of a single relaxation time is adequate.

Resonance Spectra

Some of the mechanisms of polarization, discussed in later chapters, may lead to resonance effects. Such effects will be characterized by a sharp increase in the loss factor of the specimen, accompanied by a rapid variation in the real part of the permittivity. The appropriate equivalent circuit will be a combination of inductance, L, capacitance, C, and resistance, R, the simplest of which is the series resonant circuit. Its admittance is given by

$$Y = \frac{1}{R + j\left(\omega L - \dfrac{1}{\omega C}\right)} \tag{3.21}$$

and at the resonance frequency, ω_0, $\omega_0 L = 1/\omega_0 C$ and the admittance is a maximum. We may rewrite equation (3.21) as

$$Y = \frac{1}{R\left\{1 + jQ\left(\dfrac{\omega}{\omega_0} - \dfrac{\omega_0}{\omega}\right)\right\}},$$

$$Y = \frac{\dfrac{1}{R}\left\{1 - jQ\left(\dfrac{\omega}{\omega_0} - \dfrac{\omega_0}{\omega}\right)\right\}}{1 + Q^2\left(\dfrac{\omega}{\omega_0} - \dfrac{\omega_0}{\omega}\right)^2} \tag{3.22}$$

where $Q = \omega_0 L/R$ is the magnification factor of the circuit.

Equating (3.22) to $j\omega C_0(\epsilon' - j\epsilon'')$ we have

$$\epsilon' = \frac{\dfrac{Q}{\omega C_0 R}\left(\dfrac{\omega_0}{\omega} - \dfrac{\omega}{\omega_0}\right)}{1 + Q^2\left(\dfrac{\omega}{\omega_0} - \dfrac{\omega_0}{\omega}\right)^2} \tag{3.23}$$

$$\epsilon'' = \frac{1}{\omega C_0 R\left\{1 + Q^2\left(\dfrac{\omega}{\omega_0} - \dfrac{\omega_0}{\omega}\right)^2\right\}} \tag{3.24}$$

and
$$\tan \delta = \frac{1}{Q\left(\dfrac{\omega_0}{\omega} - \dfrac{\omega}{\omega_0}\right)}. \qquad (3.25)$$

We also have the well-known relation for a series circuit

$$Q = \frac{\omega_0}{\text{bandwidth}} \qquad (3.26)$$

where the bandwidth is the width, in frequency, of the resonance curve at 3 dB down, i.e. at the points where the current has fallen to $\sqrt{2}$ of its maximum value.

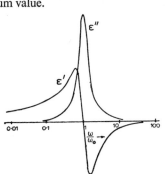

Fig. 13. Frequency response of an R-L-C equivalent circuit

Equations (3.23) to (3.26) may be used to determine the equivalent circuit of a particular dielectric exhibiting resonance, providing C_0 is known. The angular frequency at which maximum ϵ'' occurs is ω_0 and, from (3.24),

$$\epsilon''_{max} = \frac{1}{\omega_0 C_0 R} \qquad (3.27)$$

from which R is determined. By measurement of the 3 dB bandwidth Q is determined, from which we get L via $Q = \omega_0 L/R$. Finally C is obtained from $\omega_0 = 1\sqrt{LC}$. If C_0 is unknown it appears as a parameter in the values obtained.

In practice it is not often necessary to obtain the equivalent resonant circuit of a dielectric. The more usual problem is to decide whether a given frequency spectrum represents a relaxation or a resonance. Equations (3.23) and (3.24) are plotted in Fig. 13 from which it will be seen that the most obvious feature is the change of sign of ϵ' at resonance. This is generally called anomalous dispersion and, in practice, is found superposed on a 'background', steady value of ϵ', so that the total curve for the real part of permittivity does not cross the zero axis. This will be dealt with further when we consider mechanisms of polarization in more detail.

CHAPTER 4

Mechanisms of Polarization

Frequency-dependence of Permittivity

We saw, in the previous chapter, that the permittivity of dielectrics varies with frequency. Spectra are obtained which can be characterized as relaxation processes or as resonances and, in order to account for these, it is necessary to propose models which will describe the atomic and molecular processes of polarization.

The spectra themselves suggest the types of model which may be used. A pair of opposite charges, separated by a small distance, form an electric dipole. This may be imagined as free to rotate to align itself with a field. If the field is an alternating one the dipole will keep on rotating in sympathy with it; a resonance will occur when the applied field has a frequency equal to the natural rotational frequency of the dipole. If the dipole is imagined to be in a medium presenting heavy frictional damping on its rotation, its response to the field will be of the relaxation type, the rotation falling further and further in phase behind the applied field.

Rotation is only one of the possible modes of vibration which may be imagined for the dipole. It may also act as a linear harmonic oscillator in which the distance between the charges varies under the influence of an applied field. Again resonance or relaxation behaviour is possible, depending on the nature of the damping present.

Thus in examining the atomic and molecular structures of the dielectric we will be looking for those which may give rise to electric dipole behaviour.

Polarizability

On the macroscopic scale we have defined the polarization, $\mathbf{P}$, to represent the bound charges at the surface of the material such that

$$\mathbf{P} = (\epsilon' - 1)\,\epsilon_0\,\mathbf{E} \text{ coulomb metre}^{-1}. \qquad (4.1)$$

Two electric charges, of opposite polarity, $\pm Q$, separated by a distance d, represent a dipole of moment μ, given by

$$\mu = Qd. \tag{4.2}$$

The moment is a vector which is taken to have the direction from the negative to the positive charge.

Now we have, in the polarized dielectric, P bound charges per unit area and if we take two unit areas, on opposite faces of a cube, separated by a distance l, the moment due to unit area will be

$$\mu = \mathbf{P}.l. \tag{4.3}$$

For unit distance between the unit areas $l = 1$ and we have $\mu = \mathbf{P}$ per unit volume. Thus the polarization P is identical with the electric moment per unit volume of the material. This moment may be thought of as resulting from the additive action of N elementary dipoles per unit volume, each of average moment $\overline{\mu}$, therefore

$$\mathbf{P} = N\overline{\mu}. \tag{4.4}$$

Furthermore, μ may be assumed to be proportional to a local electric field *inside* the dielectric. If this is denoted by $\mathbf{E}_{int}$, being the value of the field acting on the dipole, we define

$$\mu = \alpha \mathbf{E}_{int} \tag{4.5}$$

where α is called the *polarizability* of the dipole, i.e. is the average dipole moment per unit field strength. The dimensions of α are

$$\frac{\text{sec}^2 \text{ coulomb}^2}{\text{kilograms}} = \epsilon - \text{metre}^3.$$

Thus we have

$$\mathbf{P} = (\epsilon' - 1)\,\epsilon_0\,\mathbf{E} = N\alpha\mathbf{E}_{int}. \tag{4.6}$$

This is referred to as the Clausius equation.

Since α is defined in terms of dipole moment, its magnitude will clearly be a measure of the extent to which electric dipoles are formed by the atoms and molecules. These may arise through a variety of mechanisms, any or all of which contribute to the value of α. Thus, for convenience, we regard the total polarizability to be the sum of individual polarizabilities each arising from one particular model, i.e.

$$\alpha = \alpha_e + \alpha_a + \alpha_d + \alpha_i$$

where the terms on the right-hand side are the individual polarizabilities, which will now be discussed.

Optical Polarizability (α_e)

An atom comprises a positively charged inner shell surrounded by electron clouds having symmetries determined by their quantum states. When a field is applied, the electron clouds are displaced slightly with respect to the positive cores, causing the atoms to take on an induced dipole moment. This induced moment has all the characteristics of an assembly of dipoles produced by elastic displacement of electrons, which have natural frequencies equal to, or higher than, those of visible light. The strength of the induced moment, μ_e, for an atom is proportional to the local field in the region of the atom and is given by

$$\mu_e = \alpha_e E_{int}$$

where α_e is called the *optical polarizability*; it is sometimes also referred to as the *electronic polarizability*.

Molecular Polarizability

Consider a diatomic molecule made up of atoms A and B. Because of the interaction between them there is a redistribution of electrons between the constituent atoms which should, generally, be axially symmetrical along AB. It may be expected that the diatomic molecule will possess a dipole moment in the direction AB, except where the atoms A and B are identical, when the dipole moment should vanish for reasons of symmetry. Molecules having a large dipole moment are described as 'polar', an example being hydrochloric acid in which there is a displacement of charge in the bonding between H and the Cl atoms. This gives rise to a configuration in which a positive charge is separated from a negative charge by a small distance, thus forming a true dipole.

Under the influence of an applied field the polarization of a polar substance will change by virtue of two possible mechanisms. Firstly, the field may cause the atoms to be displaced, altering the distance between them and hence changing the dipole moment of the molecule. This mechanism is called *atomic polarizability* (α_a).

Secondly, the molecule as a whole may rotate about its axis of symmetry, so that the dipole aligns itself with the field. This is referred to as *orientational polarizability* (α_d).

Interfacial Polarizability (α_i)

In a real crystal there inevitably exists a large number of defects such as lattice vacancies, impurity centres, dislocations and so on. Free charge carriers, migrating through the crystal, under the influence of an applied field, may be trapped by, or pile up against a defect. The effect of this will be the creation of a localized accumulation of charge which will induce its image charge on an electrode and give rise to a dipole moment. This constitutes a separate mechanism of polarization in the crystal, and is given the name *interfacial polarizability* (α_i).

Any or all of the above mechanisms may contribute to the behaviour of an applied field. As has been described earlier, they are lumped together in a phenomenological constant α, the polarizability, defined by equation (4.5).

Classification of Dielectrics

The three atomic or molecular polarizabilities, α_e, α_a and α_d, lead to a general classification of dielectric materials. All dielectrics will fall into one of three groups:

(a) Non-polar materials which show variations of permittivity at frequencies in the optical range.

(b) Polar materials having variation of permittivity in the infra-red as well as the optical region.

(c) Dipolar materials which, in addition, show orientational polarization.

In materials of class (a) the electric field produces an elastic displacement of electrons only. In this group will be found all those dielectrics having a single type of atom whether they be solids, liquids or gases.

In class (b), the 'polar' materials, dipolar groups of atoms may exist, but these groups show only elastic displacements. The natural frequencies of the molecular dipoles are generally in the infra-red range and the materials are characterized by infra-red absorption. It should be noted, however, that if there are several possible equilibrium positions for the groups of atoms comprising the dipole, the substance belongs to group (c). Materials falling into group (b) include all substances having molecules whose net dipole moment is zero, even though they comprise dipolar groups of atoms. Examples of these are CO_2, paraffins, benzene C_6H_6, carbon tetrachloride CCl_4 and many oils. In most of these the infra-red polarizability is only a fraction of optical polarizability and, from the practical point of view, their behaviour is very similar to that of non-polar materials.

The most important members of this group, however, are the ionic solids, such as rock-salt, the alkali halide crystals in general, TiO_2 etc. These all show very large infra-red polarizabilities.

Class (c) embraces all materials consisting of dipolar molecules; at low temperatures these may become polar solids by freezing-in of the molecules so that they are no longer able to rotate to align themselves with the field. In some cases, however, such as ice, the turning of the dipole may be obtained by transfer of an ion from one equilibrium site to another.

The determination of dipole moment of a molecule can lead to interesting information on its structure. The fact that CO_2 does not possess a permanent dipole moment suggests that the three atoms must be arranged in a straight line with the carbon atom half-way between the two oxygen atoms. On the other hand H_2O has a permanent moment, which means that the two hydrogen atoms and oxygen are arranged at the corners of a triangle. This sort of study is the province of stereochemistry in which measurements of dipole moment are an important technique.

Studies of this sort have led to the discovery of two qualitative rules for large molecules. Such molecules often contain a number of dipolar molecular groups such as the hydroxyl group O—H, or the ketone group C=O. The rule states that, to a fair approximation, these groups contribute the same dipole moment in whatever molecule they occur. The total moment of the molecule is then simply the vector sum of the moments of all the groups present.

The second rule relates to optical polarizability and is based on the fact that the distribution of electrons in certain molecular groups is approximately independent of the type of molecule in which they occur. Thus the optical polarizability from, say, a ketone group $C\!\!=\!\!O$ will be much the same whether it is in the gas CO_2 or a molecule such as $C_{10}H_{16}O_2$. It should be noted, however, that the polarizability of such groups often depends on direction. For the ketone groups the polarizability in the direction of the line connecting the two atoms would be different from that in the direction perpendicular to it.

The Problems of Dielectric Theory

The purpose of dielectric theory must be to permit calculation of the electric dipole moment, induced in the material by the application of a field, from its atomic and molecular structure. This will be done by calculating the polarizability which has been defined in such a way that it is the link between the microscopic and the macroscopic behaviour of the dielectric, the latter being described by its permittivity.

The calculation from an atomic or molecular model of explicit values of permittivity and its frequency and temperature dependence, is beset by considerable difficulties, and approximations are generally used. For example, in the case of atomic polarizability no calculation could be made unless the precise configurations of the positive ionic cores and their electron clouds were known, and this is possible only in a limited number of relatively simple cases. In general, therefore, a simple model is chosen to represent a material of much greater complexity; this usually allows approximate formulae to be derived describing the dielectric behaviour, and comparison of these with the experimental results indicates the validity of the model used. The following chapters illustrate the methods used.

CHAPTER 5

The Effective Field

Introduction

In the previous chapter we established the Clausius equation (4.6) relating the macroscopic parameter ϵ', with proposed molecular parameters α and E_{int}. In order to calculate these, a model is required which will be derived from the physical behaviour of the dielectric.

In the dielectric there exist two different types of interaction forces. Those due to chemical bonds, van der Waals attraction and atomic forces of repulsion, are essentially short-range, only being effective between nearest neighbours. Forces due to interaction between electrostatic dipoles are, compared with these, of very long range. Because of this, an accurate calculation of the interaction of a particular dipole with all the other dipoles of the specimen would be very complicated. However, a very good approximation can be made by considering that, beyond a certain distance from the given dipole, the dielectric can be represented by a continuous polarized dielectric medium having the macroscopic dielectric properties of the specimen. This method was adopted by H. A. Lorentz to calculate the internal field proposed by Mosotti in 1850.

The Lorentz Equation

Referring to Fig. 14, consider a molecule A to be at the centre of a spherical hole in the polarized dielectric. Assuming, for the moment, that the hole is empty of other molecules, the field on A will be the applied field $\mathbf{E}$ plus a contribution, $\mathbf{E}_d$, due to the ends of the dipole chains which terminate on the surface of the sphere. Now, by definition of $\mathbf{P}$, the charge density on the spherical surface will be P per unit area, and each element of area dA will contribute a radial field at A whose magnitude is given by

$$dE_d = \frac{P\cos\theta}{4\pi\epsilon_0 r^2}dA \qquad (5.1)$$

where r is the radius of the sphere and θ is the angle between the direction of the polarization vector in the medium and the radius from A to the area dA. Taking the field at A due to all the elements dA, the horizontal components will, for reasons of symmetry, cancel and the vertical components will add. The magnitude of each vertical component will be $dE_d \cos \theta$, so that we have

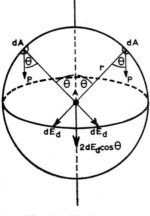

$$E_d = \oint_{\text{Sphere}} \frac{P \cos^2 \theta \, dA}{4\pi \epsilon_0 r^2}$$

$$= \int_0^\pi \frac{P \cos^2 \theta \cdot 2\pi r^2 \sin \theta \, d\theta}{4\pi \epsilon_0 r^2},$$

i.e. $E_d = \dfrac{1}{3}\dfrac{P}{\epsilon_0} = \dfrac{E}{3}(\epsilon' - 1).$ (5.2)

Fig. 14. The Lorentz equation

The reference molecule, A, is not in fact surrounded by empty space but by other molecules, which must contribute to the local field at A. The proposal made by Mosotti was that, on average, the effects of all the near neighbours cancelled so that this contribution could be regarded as negligible. This is, in most cases, an unwarrantable assumption, but may apply to gases at low pressure. Working on this basis, the total field acting upon A will be given by

$$E_{\text{int}} = E + \frac{E}{3}(\epsilon' - 1)$$

i.e. $$E_{\text{int}} = \frac{E}{3}(\epsilon' + 2) \qquad (5.3)$$

the so-called 'Mosotti Field'.

Inserting this into equation (4.6) we have

$$P = N\alpha E_{\text{int}} = N\alpha \frac{E}{3}(\epsilon' + 2)$$

but
$$\mathbf{P} = (\epsilon' - 1)\,\epsilon_0\,\mathbf{E}$$

so that
$$\frac{N\alpha}{3\epsilon_0} = \frac{\epsilon' - 1}{\epsilon' + 2}. \tag{5.4}$$

For gases at low pressure (to which the Mosotti field is most likely to apply) ϵ' will have a value very close to unity, so that $\epsilon' + 2 \doteqdot 3$. Then (5.4) may be approximated to

$$\frac{N\alpha}{\epsilon_0} = \epsilon' - 1 = \chi \tag{5.5}$$

where χ is the dielectric susceptibility of the gas.

By definition, N is the number of molecules per unit volume. If we multiply this by M, the molecular weight of the material, and divide by the density, ρ, we have the number of molecules per gram-molecule, i.e. Avogadro's number N_0 ($= 6\cdot023 \times 10^{23}$). Using this in (5.4) we have the polarizability per gram-molecule

$$\Pi = \frac{N_0\,\alpha}{3\epsilon_0} = \frac{\epsilon' - 1}{\epsilon' + 2}\frac{M}{\rho}\;\text{metre}^3. \tag{5.6}$$

This is called the 'Clausius-Mosotti' equation, in which the polarizability, α, is the only unknown quantity.

So far, both in the discussion in the previous chapter of the Clausius equation and in the above work, we have treated the relative permittivity as being represented simply by the real part ϵ'. In a practical material with losses, ϵ'' will be finite and, from equation (5.6) α will be complex. Thus, for generality, (5.6) should be written

$$\Pi = \frac{N_0\,\alpha}{3\epsilon_0} = \frac{\epsilon_r - 1}{\epsilon_r + 2}\frac{M}{\rho}. \tag{5.7}$$

This equation also applies in the optical frequency range. For a plane electromagnetic wave in a continuous medium, the velocity of propagation is given by

$$v = \frac{1}{(\mu\epsilon)^{1/2}} = \frac{1}{(\mu_0\,\mu_r\,\epsilon_0\,\epsilon_r)^{1/2}}. \tag{5.8}$$

The refractive index of a medium with respect to free space is given by the ratio of the velocity of the wave in free space to that in the medium, i.e.

$$\text{refractive index} = n = \frac{1/(\mu_0 \epsilon_0)^{1/2}}{1/(\mu_0 \mu_r \epsilon_0 \epsilon_r)^{1/2}} = (\mu_r \epsilon_r)^{1/2}.$$

Since, for dielectric media $\mu_r = 1$, we have

$$n^2 = \epsilon_r \tag{5.9}$$

which is known as the Maxwell relation, and, for optical frequencies, (5.7) may be written as

$$\Pi = \frac{N_0 \alpha}{3\epsilon_0} = \frac{n^2 - 1}{n^2 + 2} \frac{M}{\rho} \tag{5.10}$$

This is known as the Lorentz equation and was developed independently by H. A. Lorentz and also by L. Lorenz.

The assumptions implicit in the derivation of the Clausius-Mosotti formula are as follows:

(i) Polarization of the molecules by elastic displacement only, since this is assumed to be the mechanism whereby the dipole moment will be proportional to the field:

(ii) absence of short-range (non-dipolar) interactions;

(iii) isotropy of the polarizability of the molecule;

(iv) isotropy of the arrangement of the molecules.

All these conditions are fulfilled by the rare gases, but by little else.

The test of the formula will be the measurement of dielectric constant over a range of densities. If each set of measurements gives a constant value for the molar polarizability Π, equation (5.6) is confirmed. This has been done for the following gases, and the values in cm^3 found for their polarizabilities have been given as:

He (0·5), Ne (1·0), Ar (4·2), Kr (6·3), Xe (10).

The increase of polarizability with molecular weight is also predicted by (5.6), and is due to the increase in the number of electrons per atom. The formula holds over a very wide range of densities; molar polarizability for O_2 at one atmosphere is 3·869 and is 3·878 for the liquid. The above conditions for the applicability of (5·7) limit it to non-dipolar molecules so that $\alpha = (\alpha_e + \alpha_a)$ only. Since the Maxwell relation (5.9) is derived from considerations of atomic not molecular structure, the Lorentz-Lorenz relation (5.10) will apply only for the case $\alpha = \alpha_e$. Thus, if we take the polarizability from measurements of permittivity at radio frequency, when both electronic and atomic polarization can operate, and compare it with the value calculated from the optical refractive index, n, we will have a measure of the proportion of total polarizability due to atomic displacement.

Since atomic polarizability is characterized by a marked absorption in the infra-red band, a material exhibiting little such absorption should be expected to give the same result for α at radio and optical frequencies, whilst one with a marked absorption should not. This is borne out in practice, for example pentane (C_5H_{12}) has little infra-red absorption and gives $\epsilon_r = 1·82$ and $n^2 = 1·85$ so that the calculated α is much the same from equations (5.7) and (5.10). On the other hand CO_2 has a marked infra-red absorption and polarizability calculated from ϵ_r is about 10% higher than that calculated from n^2.

We will now consider the calculation of the individual polarizabilities which will go to make up the total polarizability α.

Electronic Polarizability

The simplest model on which to base a calculation of electronic polarizability is that which may be taken to apply approximately to a monatomic gas, namely, a positive atomic core carrying at charge $+Ze$ surrounded by a spherical negative cloud of charge having the magnitude $-Ze$. This corresponds roughly to the quantum picture for gases having electrons in s states only, these being spherically symmetrical, in the absence of interation between atoms.

As a further simplification, for the initial calculation, we will assume the charge cloud to be of uniform density and of radius r_0. An external field $\mathbf{E}$ will exert a force of magnitude $Ze\mathbf{E}$ on the cloud and will displace it so that its centre no longer coincides with the nucleus, as shown in Fig. 15. If the displacement is a distance d then the proportion of the negative charge within a sphere of radius d can be regarded as concentrated at the new centre of the cloud giving rise to an attractive force between it and the nucleus. The magnitude of the displaced charge will be given by

$$Q_d = -Ze \cdot \frac{4\pi d^3/3}{4\pi r_0^3/3} = \frac{-Zed^3}{r_0^3}. \tag{5.11}$$

The magnitude of coulomb attraction between this, treated as concentrated at a point, and the nucleus will be

$$F = \frac{Q_d Ze}{4\pi\epsilon_0 d^2} = \frac{-(Ze)^2 d}{4\pi\epsilon_0 r_0^3} \tag{5.12}$$

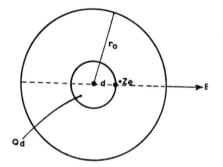

Fig. 15. Electronic polarizability

but this must balance the force on the charge cloud due to the field **E** which is $-Ze\mathbf{E}$, thus

$$-Ze\mathbf{E} = \frac{-(Ze)^2 \mathbf{d}}{4\pi\epsilon_0 r_0^3}$$

or

$$Ze\mathbf{d} = 4\pi\epsilon_0 r_0^3 \mathbf{E}. \tag{5.13}$$

Now the dipole moment, induced by the field, will be given by

$$\mathbf{\mu} = Ze\mathbf{d} = \alpha_e \mathbf{E}. \tag{5.14}$$

Combining (5.13) and (5.14) we have an expression for the optical polarizability

$$\alpha_e = 4\pi\epsilon_0 r_0^3. \tag{5.15}$$

The molecular polarizability for a monatomic gas is given by (5.6) as $N_0\alpha/3\epsilon_0$; using this in (5.15) yields

$$\Pi = N_0 \cdot \frac{4\pi}{3} = r_0^3 \qquad (5.16)$$

and, since N_0 is the number of molecules in a gram molecule, Π is seen to be equal to that total volume of gas molecules present.

The assumption, on which this calculation is based, that the spherical charge cloud, surrounding the nucleus, has a uniform charge density is not in accord with the quantum picture of the atom. The latter predicts a maximum probability density at a given radius corresponding to the first Bohr orbit – with an exponential falling off of density at greater radii. The full calculation (see, for instance, Van Vleck[11]) predicts a molar polarizability for atomic hydrogen of 1·68, whilst equation (5.16) gives the value 0·378 cm³. Unfortunately it is not possible to subject this to an experimental test, since atomic hydrogen gas does not exist, the atoms always forming diatomic molecules. It is easy to explain the larger value of polarizability predicted by quantum theory since, on this model, the outermost regions of the probability density cloud correspond to the electron being weakly bonded to the parent nucleus. Under this circumstance the electron may be assumed to be more affected by the applied field; thus the few electrons in this state will contribute more to the polarizability than will those close to the nucleus.

Temperature-dependence of Static Permittivity

In the foregoing discussion of the polarizability of non-polar gases, the theory has no indication of a temperature variation of permittivity, and this is borne out in practice.

For polar molecules, however, polarizability is inversely proportional to temperature, showing that the orientational polarization mechanism is temperature-dependent. Using the statistical theory of orientation, developed by Langevin for magnetic dipoles, Debye set up a theoretical model for molecules carrying a permanent electric dipole moment.

In order to simplify the calculation it is assumed that the density of the gas is sufficiently low that the dipolar interaction energy is small compared with $k\mathrm{T}$, the thermal energy of a single dipole at thermal equilibrium, where k is Boltzmann's constant and T the absolute temperature.

When an electric field is applied the dipoles all experience a torque tending to align them with the field. It is assumed that they are free to take up any direction with respect to the applied field.

The potential energy U, of a dipole of moment μ, whose axis makes an angle θ with a field $\mathbf{E}$, is

$$U = -\mu E \cos \theta.$$

If all the dipoles are assumed to be concentrated at a point at the centre of a sphere of unit radius, Boltzmann's statistics gives the number n, whose axes point between angles θ and $(\theta + d\theta)$, with respect to $\mathbf{E}$, as

$$n = A \exp\left(\frac{-U}{kT}\right).d\Omega$$

where $d\Omega = 2\pi \sin \theta d\theta$ is the solid angle corresponding to $d\theta$, and A is a constant, i.e.

$$n = A \exp\left(\frac{\mu E \cos \theta}{kT}\right) 2\pi \sin \theta d\theta. \tag{5.17}$$

The total number of dipoles within the sphere will be given by integrating the expression for n from 0 to π. Each dipole contributes a moment $\mu \cos \theta$ in the direction of the field, and the total moment of those within the solid angle $d\Omega$ will be $n\mu \cos \theta$. The net moment of the assembly will be, therefore, the integral from 0 to π of $n\mu \cos \theta$. The average moment per dipole, μ_d in the direction of the field will be given by

$$\frac{\text{net moment of the assembly}}{\text{total number of dipoles}}.$$

Thus

$$\mu_d = \frac{\int_0^\pi A \exp\left(\frac{\mu E \cos \theta}{kT}\right)(\mu \cos \theta) 2\pi \sin \theta d\theta}{\int_0^\pi A \exp\left(\frac{\mu E \cos \theta}{kT}\right) 2\pi \sin \theta d\theta}. \tag{5.18}$$

The ratio μ_d/μ will be a measure of the net polarization of the gas due to the application of the field $\mathbf{E}$ where μ is taken to be the average value of the dipole moment of each molecule. The evaluation of the integrals in (5.18) is a standard piece of work (see, for instance, von Hippel[1], p. 148) and gives the result

$$\frac{\bar{\mu}_d}{\mu} = \coth x - \frac{1}{x} \tag{5.19}$$

where $x = \mu E/kT$. This is known as the Langevin function. If we substitute the known experimental values for, say HCl, of $\mu = 3 \cdot 7 \times 10^{-30}$ coulombs/m, the field required to produce a 50% polarization $\{(\bar{\mu}_d/\mu) = \frac{1}{2}\}$ is approximately 2×10^7 V/cm. Thus it is seen that, in fields likely to be encountered experimentally, the degree of polarization will always be small. For such fields $x \ll 1$ and the Langevin expression may be approximated to

$$\bar{\mu}_d = \frac{\mu^2}{3kT}.\mathbf{E} \tag{5.20}$$

and the orientational polarization is seen to be inversely proportional to absolute temperature. Since the distortional polarization – arising from displacement of the atoms or electrons by the field – is temperature-independent, plotting the polarizability as a function of temperature provides a convenient method of separating the distortional and orientational contributions.

We make use of equation (5.7) for the polarizability per gram-molecule

$$\Pi = \frac{N_0 \alpha}{3\epsilon_0} \doteqdot \frac{\epsilon_r - 1}{3} \frac{M}{\rho} \tag{5.21}$$

where, for a gas, $(\epsilon_r + 2) \doteqdot 3$ and α is the total polarizability, given by

$$\alpha = \alpha_e + \alpha_a + \frac{\mu^2}{3kT}. \tag{5.22}$$

Experimentally the static relative permittivity ϵ_s' will be measured over a range of temperatures and the results used to plot Π against reciprocal temperature. The intercept of the extrapolated curve with the Π-axis at $1/T = 0$ gives $N_0(\alpha_e + \alpha_a)/3\epsilon_0$ and the slope of the curve gives $(\mu^2/3k)(N_0/3\epsilon_0)$. The latter result therefore yields the value of the dipole moment of the molecule. The values of the fixed constants in the expression are

$$\frac{N_0}{3\epsilon_0} = 2 \cdot 27 \times 10^{34}; \qquad \frac{N_0}{9\epsilon_0 k} = 5 \cdot 48 \times 10^{56}.$$

As has been discussed earlier in this chapter, the square of the optical refractive index of the dielectric gives the contribution due to electronic polarizability. Knowing the orientational contribution from the temperature-dependent component, the atomic polarizability may be deduced.

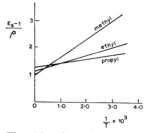

In Fig. 16 $(\epsilon_s - 1/\rho)$ is plotted against $1000/T$ for three gases, at moderate pressures and constant density. These show the simple theory to be well-fulfilled in the case of dipolar gases.

Fig. 16. $(\epsilon_s - 1/\rho)$ against $1/T \times 10^3$ for methyl, ethyl and propyl ether

The decrease in $\epsilon_s - 1/\rho$, at lower temperatures, in going from methyl to ethyl to propyl is proportional to the increasing molecular weight through the series. At high temperatures the major contribution to ϵ_s is from the free electrons, and the gas with the larger number of electrons gives the higher value.

Spontaneous Polarization

It was pointed out, when deducing the Mosotti expression for the internal field in a dielectric, that the assumptions on which it was based could apply only to non-dipolar molecules. It is, nevertheless, of interest to explore the implications of a Mosotti field in a dipolar material for which the Langevin expression would apply.

Clausius' equation (4.6) relates polarization and polarizability by

$$\mathbf{P} = (\epsilon' - 1)\epsilon_0 \mathbf{E} = N\alpha \mathbf{E}_{int}. \qquad (5.23)$$

If we assume an internal field of the Mosotti type

$$\mathbf{E}_{int} = \mathbf{E} + \frac{\mathbf{P}}{3\epsilon_0}$$

we get, from (5.23),

$$\mathbf{P} = \frac{N\alpha E}{1 - \dfrac{N\alpha}{3\epsilon_0}} \qquad (5.24)$$

and

$$\chi = \epsilon' - 1 = \frac{N\alpha/e_0}{1 - \dfrac{N\alpha}{3\epsilon_0}}. \qquad (5.25)$$

The right-hand sides of both equations (5.24) and (5.25) will tend to infinity as $N\alpha/3\epsilon_0 \to 1$.

If

$$\alpha = \alpha_e + \alpha_a + \frac{\mu^2}{3kT}$$

it is clearly possible that there will be a critical temperature T_c for which $N\alpha/3\epsilon_0 = 1$, given by

$$T_c = \frac{N\mu^2}{9\epsilon_0 k} \cdot \frac{1}{1 - \dfrac{N(\alpha_e + \alpha_a)}{3\epsilon_0}}. \qquad (5.26)$$

At this temperature the expressions for both polarization and susceptibility go to infinity. The same type of behaviour is met in the theory of ferromagnetism, the critical temperature being the Curie temperature, below which the material becomes spontaneously magnetized. In this case the dielectric will become spontaneously polarized, below the Curie temperature, and by virtue of this analogy, a dielectric in which this occurs is described as ferroelectric.

The analogy may be pursued further by assuming

$$(\alpha_e + \alpha_a) \ll \mu^2/3kT$$

so that

$$\alpha \doteqdot \frac{\mu^2}{3kT} \quad \text{and} \quad T_c = \frac{N\mu^2}{9\epsilon_0 k}.$$

Substituting in (5.25) leads to

$$\chi = \frac{3T_c}{T - T_c} \qquad (5.27)$$

which is the same form of expression as the Curie-Weiss law of magnetic susceptibility.

Although the assumptions on which the Mosotti field is deduced should rule out the prediction of spontaneous polarization as invalid, ferroelectrics do exist, and are dealt with in a later chapter. For these it must be assumed that the dipolar interactions and their response to an applied field are of such a type as to provide an internal field of the Mosotti form.

The appearance of spontaneous polarization, due to the internal field, is referred to in the literature as the 'Mosotti catastrophe'.

CHAPTER 6

Orientational Polarization

Introduction

In defining complex permittivity, in Chapter 1, it was pointed out that the dielectric flux density, D, resulting from an applied alternating field E would, in general, differ in phase from E. This is due to the inertia of the polarization which, when the frequency becomes high enough, cannot follow the field variations, giving rise to a 'relaxation' of the measured permittivity.

This behaviour may be stated formally by an equation of the type

$$\epsilon(\omega) = \epsilon_\infty + \int\limits_0^\infty \alpha(t) e^{j\omega t} dt \qquad (6.1)$$

in which ϵ_∞ is the value of permittivity at infinite frequency which is a constant, and $\alpha(t)$ is some sort of decay factor accounting for the lagging of polarization behind the applied field. Clearly $\alpha(t)$ will be connected with the total permittivity such that it can be put in terms of the real and imaginary parts ϵ' and ϵ''. Also, from (6.1) we must have $\alpha(t) \to 0$ as $\omega \to \infty$ since, at $\omega = \infty$ $\epsilon(\omega) = \epsilon_\infty$.

Since it accounts for the lagging of $D(\omega)$ with respect to $E(\omega)$, $\alpha(t)$ must describe the decay of polarization after the sudden removal of a steady field. It will also describe the increase of polarization towards its equilibrium value when a steady field is suddenly applied. It may therefore be summarized as being related to the time constant of polarization of a dielectric.

The Debye Equations

Debye[12] proposed an exponential form for the decay factor

$$\alpha(t) = \alpha(0) e^{-t/\tau} \qquad (6.2)$$

67

where τ is a relaxation time, characteristic of the dielectric, which may be a function of temperature but not of time.

Inserting this in (6.1) we have

$$\epsilon_r(\omega) = \epsilon_\infty + \int_0^\infty \alpha(0) e^{(j\omega - 1/\tau)t} dt \qquad (6.3)$$

which, on integration, yields

$$\epsilon_r(\omega) = \epsilon_\infty + \frac{\alpha(0)}{\left(\dfrac{1}{\tau} - j\omega\right)}. \qquad (6.4)$$

At $\omega = 0$ $\epsilon_r(\omega) = \epsilon_s$ and we have

$$\epsilon_s = \epsilon_\infty + \tau\alpha(0). \qquad (6.5)$$

Putting (6.5) in (6.2)

$$\alpha(t) = \frac{\epsilon_s - \epsilon_\infty}{\tau} e^{-t/\tau}. \qquad (6.6)$$

Using (6.6) in (6.1) we have

$$\epsilon_r(\omega) = \epsilon_\infty + \int_0^\infty \frac{\epsilon_s - \epsilon_\infty}{\tau} e^{-t/\tau} e^{j\omega t} dt$$

$$\therefore \quad \epsilon_r(\omega) = \epsilon' - j\epsilon'' = \epsilon_\infty + \frac{\epsilon_s - \epsilon_\infty}{1 - j\omega\tau}. \qquad (6.7)$$

Equating real and imaginary parts

$$\epsilon' = \epsilon_\infty + \frac{\epsilon_s - \epsilon_\infty}{1 + \omega^2 \tau^2} \qquad (6.8)$$

$$\epsilon'' = \frac{(\epsilon_s - \epsilon_\infty) \omega\tau}{1 + \omega^2 \tau^2} \qquad (6.9)$$

and $\tan \delta = \dfrac{\epsilon''}{\epsilon'} = \dfrac{(\epsilon_s - \epsilon_\infty) \omega\tau}{\epsilon_s + \epsilon_\infty \omega^2 \tau^2}. \qquad (6.10)$

Equations (6.8)–(6.10) are known as the Debye equations.

Referring back to the equivalent circuit treatment of Chapter 3 it will be seen that, if equations (3.15) and (3.16) are substituted in equations (3.12) to (3.14) the latter become identical with (6.8)–(6.10). Thus the Debye equations are seen to describe a relaxation spectrum.

It remains to propose atomic models which would account for an exponential decay factor.

The Potential Double Well

In this model the dielectric is taken to comprise a collection of non-interacting particles, each of which has two possible equilibrium positions separated by a high potential barrier. Such a model would apply, for instance, to a dipole having equilibrium positions corresponding to its axis being at $0°$ and $180°$ to some given direction.

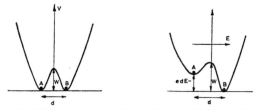

Fig. 17. Potential double well (a) without field, (b) with field E

We will consider a charged particle to have two equilibrium positions A and B a distance d apart, with a potential barrier $W \gg kT$, between them as represented diagrammatically in Fig. 17(a). In the absence of an applied field it is assumed to have the same potential in each position and will oscillate about either with an energy of the order of the Boltzmann energy kT. Occasionally, due to some fluctuation, such as a series of energetically advantageous collisions, the particle may acquire sufficient energy to jump over the barrier into the other equilibrium position. On time average, for thermal equilibrium, it will remain near A as long as near B and the probability of finding it near either A or B is $\frac{1}{2}$.

When a field $\mathbf{E}$ is applied, the potentials V_A and V_B of the particle, of charge e, at A and B will differ by an amount

$$V_A - V_B = \mathbf{e}\mathbf{d}.\mathbf{E} \tag{6.11}$$

where **d** is the distance from A to B as shown in Fig. 17(b). Now from Boltzmann statistics, the probability of finding a particle with energy V is proportional to $e^{-V/kT}$, and, for E in the direction AB, (6.11) states that V_A is higher than V_B by an amount edE, so that there is now a greater probability of finding the particle in the vicinity of B than near A.

This redistribution can only come about by virtue of the small fraction of particles which acquire sufficient energy to cross the barrier of energy W. Again this number will be proportional to the Boltzmann factor $e^{-W/kt}$, in the absence of a field. When the field is applied such that V_A is increased by edE, the number making the transition from A to B will be proportional to $e^{-(W-edE)/kT}$ whilst the number from B to A will still be proportional to $e^{-W/kT}$.

It was assumed, initially, that the particles oscillated about their equilibrium positions with a frequency $\omega_0/2\pi$ due to thermal agitation. In the absence of a barrier, therefore, the probability per second of the particle moving from A to B or B to A would be $\omega_0/2\pi$. In the presence of the barrier we can write the transition probability per second as

$$P_{BA} = \frac{\omega_0}{2\pi}e^{-W/kT} \qquad (6.12)$$

for B $\rightarrow$ A, and

$$P_{AB} = \frac{\omega_0}{2\pi}e^{-(W-edE)/kT}$$

$$\doteqdot \frac{\omega_0}{2\pi}e^{-W/kT}(1+edE/kT) \qquad (6.13)$$

for A $\rightarrow$ B, where edE is assumed very small compared with kT. Using (6.12) we have

$$P_{AB} \doteqdot P_{BA}(1+edE/kT). \qquad (6.14)$$

Thus if, at any instant, there are $N_1(t)$ particles at A and $N_2(t)$ at B, a number of $N_1 P_{AB}$ will move, per second, from A to B and $N_2 P_{BA}$ from B to A, whence

$$\frac{dN_1}{dt} = -N_1 P_{AB} + N_2 P_{BA} \qquad (6.15)$$

and
$$\frac{dN_2}{dt} = +N_1 P_{AB} - N_2 P_{BA} \qquad (6.16)$$

Subtracting (6.15) from (6.16) we can write

$$\frac{d}{dt}(N_2 - N_1) = -(P_{AB} + P_{BA})(N_2 - N_1) + (P_{AB} - P_{BA})N \quad (6.17)$$

where the total number of particles $N = N_1 + N_2$ is constant. Now using (6.14), on the assumption $edE \ll kT$

$$P_{AB} + P_{BA} \doteq 2P_{BA}(1 + edE/2kT) \doteq 2P_{BA} \qquad (6.18)$$

and
$$P_{AB} - P_{BA} = \frac{edE}{kT} P_{BA}. \qquad (6.19)$$

Using (6.18) and (6.19), we have

$$\frac{d}{dt}(N_2 - N_1) = -2P_{BA}(N_2 - N_1) + 2P_{BA}\frac{edE}{2kT}N.$$

If we assume that, before the field is applied, $N_1 = N_2 = N/2$ and that the field is applied at time $t = 0$, then the above differential equation may be solved. The solution, for the value of $(N_2 - N_1)$ at a time t after application of the field, is

$$N_2 - N_1 = \frac{N}{2}\frac{edE}{kT}(1 - e^{-2P_{BA}t}). \qquad (6.20)$$

The polarization induced by the field will be proportional to $(N_2 - N_1)$ and is thus seen to increase exponentially, after application of the field, towards its equilibrium valve. The model proposed, therefore, will lead to the Debye equations.

Comparing (6.20) with the Debye decay function (6.2) and using (6.6) and (6.13), it will be seen that the relaxation time, τ, is given by

$$\tau = \frac{1}{2P_{BA}} = \frac{\pi}{\omega_0}e^{W/kT}. \qquad (6.21)$$

6

Now π/ω_0 is just the time, τ_0, of a single oscillation in the potential well which, on the Boltzmann statistical picture, is the time between successive collisions. It is assumed here that a particle executes one cycle of oscillation by starting from the vicinity of one neighbour, travelling to another and then returning to its original position. Since we have made the assumption $W \gg kT$, it follows that $\tau_0 \ll \tau$. Thus the derivation of the Debye equations from the above model will only hold if the period of the field is large compared with the average time, τ_0, between collisions.

APPLICATIONS TO REAL DIELECTRICS

Dipolar Liquids

Dielectric relaxation, in which the frequency spectrum of dielectric constant is in general agreement with the Debye formulae, is often found in dipolar liquids. This suggests a mechanism of polarization involving an exponential decay factor and Debye proposed a model for this. Since, in a liquid, the molecules are not in fixed positions, it may be imagined that if one molecule turned from its equilibrium position, its neighbours would rearrange themselves to make the new position an equilibrium one. Their average motion might be described by treating them as a continuous medium, exerting a viscous frictional damping force on the original dipole. If the dipolar molecule has radius a and moves in a continuous viscous fluid of viscosity η, the frictional constant ξ is given by Stokes law as

$$\xi = 8\pi\eta a^3 \tag{6.22}$$

If a field is applied, at an angle θ to the axis of the dipole, a torque Γ will be produced on it such that

$$\Gamma = \xi \frac{d\theta}{dt} \tag{6.23}$$

and the dipole will align itself with the field at a rate dependent upon the friction factor ξ. However, the molecular dipole is also subject to thermal fluctuations (Brownian motion) which affect the rate of change of angle when the field is applied. Debye took account of this in his calculation (which is similar to the Langevin calculation in the previous chapter) and was able to deduce an expression for the relaxation time:

$$\tau = \frac{\xi}{2kT} = \frac{4\pi\eta a^3}{kT} \tag{6.24}$$

or

$$\tau = \frac{3\eta}{kT} \cdot V \tag{6.25}$$

where V is the volume of the molecular dipole. To obtain an absolute value for τ it is necessary to know the volume of a sphere having the same frictional constant as the dipolar molecule, which is not necessarily the same as the molecular volume. Thus it is not to be expected that (6.25) will predict accurately the experimental values of relaxation time. However some agreement is obtained; for water $\eta = 0.01$ poise at room temperature and the molecular volume is approximately 3.5×10^{-23} cm^3, leading to a relaxation time $\tau \doteqdot 0.25 \times 10^{-10}$ sec. Since the maximum absorption (ϵ''_{max}) occurs at an angular frequency $\omega = 1/\tau$, we should expect relaxation in the region of 10^{10} cycles, which is agreement with experiment.

An interesting feature of equation (6.25) is its prediction that the variation, with temperature, of relaxation time, τ, should be the same as that of the coefficient of viscosity, η, divided by T. Experimentally, η is related to temperature by

$$\eta \propto \exp\left(H_\eta/kT\right)$$

where H_η is a constant for a given liquid. Thus we may predict

$$\tau \propto \frac{1}{T}\exp\left(H_\eta/kT\right)$$

and this may be tested experimentally. Since, over moderate temperature ranges, the exponential term will vary much more quickly than $1/T$, we may expect, approximately,

$$\log \tau = \frac{\text{const}}{T} \cdot$$

Measurements by Whiffen and Thompson[13] on solutions of different organic solutes in heptane obeyed this relation, as illustrated in

Fig. 18 for the case of camphor, in heptane, in which τ is plotted on a log scale against $1/T$ over the range 200°K to 350°K.

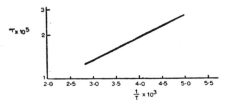

Fig. 18. Relaxation time as a function of $1/T$

Dipolar Solids

In the case of a solid, a dipole finds itself in a regular electrostatic field, due to all the other dipoles. It may have a number of equilibrium positions in this field, separated from each other by potential barriers.

In the simplest case of two equilibrium positions we have precisely the potential double-well model discussed previously. Debye type relaxation should occur for such a case.

In general, in dipolar solids, the molecular dipoles have more than two equilibrium positions, so that the frequency spectrum of permittivity is broader and flatter than predicted by the simple Debye formulae. The relaxation time, obtained from such a curve, then represents an average of a number of different relaxation times, which correspond to transitions between the different equilibrium positions. This point is discussed further in the next section.

Cole-Cole Diagrams

Cole and Cole[14] showed that a feature of relaxation behaviour, in accordance with the Debye equations, is that a graph of ϵ'' against ϵ' over the entire frequency range will always be a semicircle.

This may be seen by suitable rearrangement of equations (6.8) and (6.9) to give

$$(\epsilon' - \epsilon_\infty)^2 + (\epsilon'')^2 = \frac{(\epsilon_s - \epsilon_\infty)^2}{1 + \omega^2 \tau^2} \qquad (6.26)$$

substituting from (6.8) gives

$$(\epsilon' - \epsilon\infty)^2 + (\epsilon'')^2 = (\epsilon_s - \epsilon\infty)(\epsilon' - \epsilon\infty), \qquad (6.27)$$

i.e. $$(\epsilon')^2 - \epsilon'(\epsilon_s + \epsilon\infty) + \epsilon_s \epsilon\infty + (\epsilon'')^2 = 0. \qquad (6.28)$$

At $\omega = 0$ and $\omega = \infty$ we know that $\epsilon'' = 0$, and that $\epsilon' = \epsilon_s$ and $\epsilon\infty$ respectively. In addition at $\omega\tau = 1$, ϵ'' has its maximum value of $(\epsilon_s - \epsilon\infty)/2$ and $\epsilon' = (\epsilon_s + \epsilon\infty)/2$. If we take axes of $x = \epsilon'$ and $y = \epsilon''$,

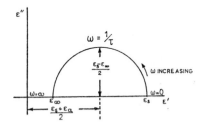

Fig. 19. Cole-Cole diagram for single relaxation time

then the above give the points $(\epsilon_s, 0)$, $(\epsilon\infty, 0)$ and $(\epsilon_s + \epsilon\infty)/2$, $(\epsilon_s - \epsilon\infty)/2$. These will be found all to lie on a circle given by

$$\left\{ x - \frac{(\epsilon_s + \epsilon\infty)}{2} \right\}^2 + y^2 = \frac{(\epsilon_s - \epsilon\infty)^2}{2} \qquad (6.29)$$

which is the equation of a circle whose centre is at the point $\{(\epsilon_s + \epsilon\infty)/2, 0\}$ and has a radius $(\epsilon_s - \epsilon\infty)/2$. This is illustrated in Fig. 19.

If (6.29) is multiplied out it gives

$$(\epsilon')^2 - \epsilon'(\epsilon_s + \epsilon\infty) + \epsilon_s \epsilon\infty + (\epsilon'')^2 = 0$$

which is the same equation as (6.28) showing that, for a Debye relaxation, the locus of $\epsilon_r = \epsilon' - j\epsilon''$, plotted on an Argand diagram, will always be a circle.

Experimentally it is often difficult to extend the frequency of an a.c. bridge measurement sufficiently high to obtain $\epsilon\infty$. If the experimental points are plotted as a Cole-Cole diagram and a semicircle drawn through them, $\epsilon\infty$ is obtained from the intercept with the x-axis.

Equations (6.8) and (6.9) can be rearranged to give

$$\epsilon' = \frac{\epsilon''}{\omega\tau} + \epsilon_\infty \qquad (6.30)$$

and

$$\epsilon' = -\omega\tau\epsilon'' + \epsilon_s. \qquad (6.31)$$

Thus the relaxation time may be obtained from the slope of a straight line drawn from the origin to a point on the circle for which ω is known.

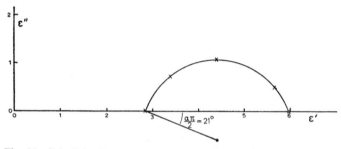
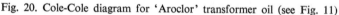

Fig. 20. Cole-Cole diagram for 'Aroclor' transformer oil (see Fig. 11)

When, as is often the case, the material has a spread of relaxation times, Cole and Cole showed that equation (6.7) should be replaced by the more general expression

$$\epsilon' - j\epsilon'' = \epsilon_\infty + \frac{\epsilon_s - \epsilon_\infty}{1 - (j\omega\tau_a)^{(1-\alpha)}} \qquad (6.32)$$

where τ_a is the mean relaxation time and α is a constant, not to be confused with polarizability, of value between 0 and 1. If the results, in such a case, are plotted in an Argand diagram the points still lie on a circle, but its centre is depressed below the ϵ'-axis.

If a radius of the circle is drawn to the points $(\epsilon_\infty, 0)$ or $(\epsilon_s, 0)$, the angle between the radius and the ϵ'-axis is equal to $\alpha(\pi/2)$.

α may be interpreted as a 'spreading factor' of the actual relaxation times about the mean value τ_a. It can be regarded as the relative width of a curve of actual relaxation time τ plotted as ordinate against $\log(\tau/\tau_a)$. These is no molecular interpretation for this factor, but it is useful in analysing a complicated relaxation spectrum, as has been done, for instance, by Davidson and Cole[15] with n-propanol.

In Fig. 20 is plotted the Cole-Cole diagram for the case of 'Aroclor' transformer oil, whose spectrum was given in Fig. 11. From the diagram, $90\alpha = 21°$, whence $\alpha = 0.23$ and there is clearly a finite spread of relaxation times.

It has been proposed by Scaife[16] that the Cole-Cole plot should be replaced by a similar plot in which the co-ordinates are the real and imaginary parts of complex polarizability. Several advantages are claimed for this. In the first place it gives more weight to high-frequency measurements, so that what appear to be small deviations in the Cole-Cole plot turn out to be important features in the α-plot. The method also provides a ready means of comparing the behaviour of substances having widely differing permittivities, since α must lie between 0 and unity. It is suggested that the α-plot provides a more stringent test of fulfilment of the Debye equations than does the Cole-Cole plot.

The Onsager Theory

In the calculation of static permittivity given in the previous chapter, it was shown how an 'effective field' inside the dielectric was calculated on the Mosotti model. Onsager[17] took this type of calculation, for spherical molecules, a stage further by taking a component of the interaction between molecules into account. This is done by replacing the Mosotti cavity, which is a mathematical fiction, with a real cavity of molecular size with a dipole at its centre. The assumptions made are that

(a) the molecule occupies a sphere of radius a and its polarizability is isotropic,

(b) the short-range interaction energy is negligible (i.e. is less than kT per molecule).

The local field acting on the molecule is made up of two parts:

(i) the field inside a cavity of radius a due to an externally applied field $\mathbf{E}$,

(ii) a reaction field due to the moment μ of the molecule itself, which sets up a polarization in the surrounding medium.

The field inside a spherical cavity may be calculated by use of Laplace's equation (1.28). Consider an uncharged sphere, of permittivity ϵ_0 and radius a, in a homogeneous field $\mathbf{E}_0$ pointing in the direction $+z$, the sphere being embedded in a medium of permittivity ϵ.

The field distribution, produced by polarization of the sphere, will be symmetrical about the z-axis, so that there will be no variation of polarization with azimuthal angle ψ. Equation (1.28) then simplifies to

$$\nabla^2 \phi = \frac{\partial^2 \phi}{\partial r^2} + \frac{z}{r} \frac{\partial \phi}{\partial r} + \frac{1}{r^2} \frac{\partial^2 \phi}{\partial \theta^2} + \frac{1}{r^2} \frac{\cos \theta}{\sin \theta} \frac{\partial \phi}{\partial \theta} = 0. \qquad (6.33)$$

If we designate the potential inside the cavity by ϕ_i, and outside by ϕ_a, the solutions of (6.33) are of the form

$$\phi_a = \left(\frac{A}{r^2} + Br \right) \cos \theta \qquad (6.34)$$

and

$$\phi_i = \left(\frac{C}{r^2} + Dr \right) \cos \theta \qquad (6.35)$$

where A, B, C and D are constants. To determine these we must consider the boundary conditions of the problem, which are:

(i) the potential must remain finite at the centre of the sphere so that for $r = 0$ $\phi_i =$ finite;

(ii) as $r \to \infty$ the external field will become unaffected by the cavity. For a given direction $r \cos \theta = z$ and $E_0 = -\partial \phi / \partial z$ so that $\phi = -E_0 z$ and $B = -E_0$ (since E_0 is in the z direction);

(iii) at $r = a$, since the field intensity is finite at the surface of the sphere, ϕ_a must become identical with ϕ_i, i.e. $\phi_i = \phi_a$ at $r = a$;

(iv) the normal component of flux must be continuous over the boundary of the sphere, i.e.

$$\frac{\epsilon \partial \phi_a}{\partial r} = \epsilon_0 \frac{\partial \phi_i}{\partial r}.$$

Using these we obtain the values of the constants as

$$A = \frac{\epsilon_0 - \epsilon}{\epsilon_0 + 2\epsilon} a^3 E_0 \left.\begin{array}{c} \\ \\ \\ \\ \end{array}\right\}$$

$$B = -E_0$$

$$C = 0 \qquad (6.36)$$

$$D = -\frac{3\epsilon}{\epsilon_0 + 2\epsilon} E_0$$

Substituting in (6.34) and (6.35)

$$\phi_a = \left(\frac{\epsilon_0 - \epsilon}{\epsilon_0 + 2\epsilon} \cdot \frac{a^3}{r^3} - 1\right) E_0 z \qquad (6.37)$$

and

$$\phi_i = -\frac{3\epsilon}{\epsilon_0 + 2\epsilon} E_0 z. \qquad (6.38)$$

The field inside the cavity, $\mathbf{E}_c$, due to the applied field $\mathbf{E}_0$ will be, from (6.38)

$$\mathbf{E}_c = -\nabla\phi_i = \frac{3\epsilon}{\epsilon_0 + 2\epsilon} \cdot \mathbf{E}_0 = \frac{3\epsilon_s}{1 + 2\epsilon_s} \cdot \mathbf{E}_0 \qquad (6.39)$$

since $\epsilon = \epsilon_0 \epsilon_s$ for the static case.

The reaction field, $\mathbf{E}_R$, due to the moment μ at the centre of the cavity may be found by a similar calculation. In this case boundary condition (i) is replaced by the requirement that the potential at $r = 0$ should be that of a point dipole of moment μ, i.e.

$$C = -\frac{\mu}{4\pi\epsilon_0}.$$

Boundary condition (ii) will be replaced by the requirement of $E_0 = 0$ for $r \to \infty$ as we are considering only the field due to the dipole, i.e. $B = 0$. This leads to an expression for the reaction field in the cavity.

$$\mathbf{E}_R = \frac{2\mu}{4\pi a^3} \cdot \frac{\epsilon_s - 1}{2\epsilon_s + 1} = \frac{2\mu}{3V} \frac{\epsilon_s - 1}{2\epsilon_s + 1} \qquad (6.40)$$

where V is the volume of the cavity.

The total field in the cavity is thus

$$\mathbf{F} = \mathbf{E}_c + \mathbf{E}_R = \frac{3\epsilon_s}{1+2\epsilon_s} \cdot \mathbf{E}_0 + \frac{2}{3V} \frac{\epsilon_s - 1}{2\epsilon_s + 1} \boldsymbol{\mu}. \tag{6.41}$$

Now this field, acting upon the dipole at the centre of the cavity, will cause its total moment to change by virtue of distortional polarization. Expressed mathematically

$$\boldsymbol{\mu} = \boldsymbol{\mu}_v + \alpha \mathbf{F} \tag{6.42}$$

where $\boldsymbol{\mu}_v$ is the original dipole moment and α is the electronic plus atomic polarizability. Using (6.41) in this we have

$$\boldsymbol{\mu} = \boldsymbol{\mu}_v + \frac{3\alpha\epsilon_s}{1+2\epsilon_s} \mathbf{E}_0 + \frac{2}{3V} \frac{(\epsilon_s - 1)}{(2\epsilon_s + 1)} \alpha\boldsymbol{\mu} \tag{6.43}$$

and solving for $\boldsymbol{\mu}$

$$\boldsymbol{\mu} = \frac{\boldsymbol{\mu}_v}{1 - \dfrac{2\alpha}{3V} \dfrac{(\epsilon_s - 1)}{(2\epsilon_s + 1)}} + \frac{3\epsilon_s}{1+2\epsilon_s} \cdot \frac{\alpha\mathbf{E}_0}{1 - \dfrac{2\alpha}{3V} \dfrac{(\epsilon_s - 1)}{(2\epsilon_s + 1)}} \tag{6.44}$$

Substituting in (6.41)

$$\mathbf{F} = \frac{3\epsilon_s}{1+2\epsilon_s} \frac{\mathbf{E}_0}{1 - \alpha g} + \frac{g}{1 - \alpha g} \boldsymbol{\mu}_v \tag{6.45}$$

where

$$g = \frac{2}{3V} \frac{(\epsilon_s - 1)}{(2\epsilon_s + 1)}. \tag{6.46}$$

Now the potential energy of a dipole of moment $\boldsymbol{\mu}_v$ in a field $\mathbf{F}$ is $-\boldsymbol{\mu}_v \cdot \mathbf{F}$ and we may calculate the average moment in the same way as was done in the Langevin calculation. It is the average moment induced by the applied field, $\mathbf{E}_0$, due to orientational polarization, which is required and so the second term of (6.45), which is independent of $\mathbf{E}_0$, must be neglected. Carrying out the Langevin calculation, with the approximation $\mu_v F/kT \ll 1$, leads to equation (5.20), i.e.

$$\boldsymbol{\mu}_v = \frac{\mu_v^2}{3kT} \mathbf{F} \tag{6.47}$$

and substituting from (6.45) without the second term gives

$$\bar{\mu}_v = \frac{3\epsilon_s}{2\epsilon_s+1} \cdot \left(\frac{\mu_v^2}{3kT(1-\alpha g)}\right) \mathbf{E}_0 \qquad (6.48)$$

and substituting in (6.44) gives the average moment, $\bar{\mu}$, of the molecule as

$$\bar{\mu} = \frac{3\epsilon_s}{2\epsilon_s+1} \left(\frac{\mu_v^2}{3kT(1-\alpha g)^2} + \frac{\alpha}{1-\alpha g}\right) \mathbf{E}_0. \qquad (6.49)$$

Now, using equation (5.4),

$$\alpha g = \frac{3\epsilon_0}{N} \cdot \frac{\epsilon_\infty - 1}{\epsilon_\infty + 2} \cdot \frac{2}{3V} \cdot \frac{\epsilon_s - 1}{2\epsilon_s + 1}$$

and since we may take $\epsilon_\infty \doteq 1$, then $\alpha g \ll 1$. Also $N\bar{\mu} = (\epsilon_s - 1)\epsilon_0 E$ so that, from (6.49)

$$\frac{(2\epsilon_s+1)(\epsilon_s-1)}{3\epsilon_s} = \frac{\mu_v^2 N}{3kT\epsilon_0}. \qquad (6.50)$$

From equation (6.50) it will be seen that, subject to the approximation $\epsilon \doteq 1$, $(\epsilon_s - 1)$ is not inversely proportional to temperature, as in the simple Langevin theory (equation 5.20), but is proportional to

$$\frac{3\epsilon_s}{(2\epsilon_s+1)} \cdot \frac{1}{T}.$$

The examples given in Fig. 16 were gases which fulfilled the requirement of no interaction between the dipoles, postulated in the derivation of the Langevin formula. Fig. 21 illustrates the case of a material conforming to the Onsager theory. This is based on measurements by Wilmot[18] on 'Aroclor 1242', which is a trichlorodiphenyl oil. From the graph it will be seen that plotting ϵ_s against $1/T$, as for the Langevin formula, does not yield a straight line, whilst plotting against

$$\frac{3\epsilon_s}{(2\epsilon_s+1)} \cdot \frac{1}{T}$$

does so. Materials showing this type of agreement are those in which there are long-range forces tending to align the dipoles, but having short-range forces between nearest neighbours which are small. Where short-range forces have to be considered as well, such as in liquid like water having hydrogen bonding, the Onsager relation will not hold. Such cases have been dealt with by Kirkwood[19] who derived a formula allowing for short-range interactions. An account of the calculations, which are somewhat complex, is given by

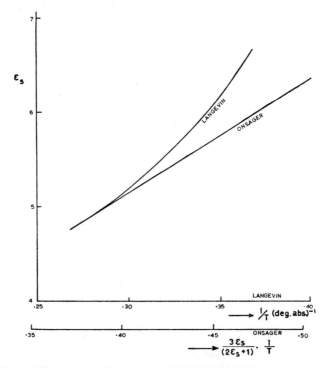

Fig. 21. Comparison of Langevin and Onsager theories for 'Aroclor 1242' (Monsanto), after Wilmot[18]

Fröhlich[20]. The Kirkwood formula provides a correct theoretical calculation of the permittivity of water, in which X-ray examination has revealed a strong correlation between the orientations of nearest-neighbour molecules, but little long-range order. It is not so successful in cases where both long- and short-range order exists.

CHAPTER 7

Distortional and Interfacial Polarization

Introduction

In considering mechanisms of polarization in Chapter 4, we identified optical and atomic polarization as arising from displacement of electrons or atoms due to the application of a field. This is called distortional polarization, distinguishing it from orientational polarization arising from rotation of the molecular dipoles.

The basic model is that of charges bound elastically to an equilibrium position. When displaced by an applied field they will return to equilibrium after removal of the field, by execution of free oscillations about their equilibrium positions, the oscillations dying out at a rate determined by the damping forces present. This model therefore leads directly to the possibility of resonance absorption, in which maximum power will be absorbed from an alternating applied field at a characteristic frequency. The charges can be regarded as behaving like linear harmonic oscillators and a mathematical formulation of their behaviour will be based on such a model.

Resonance Absorption

If a linear harmonic oscillator is disturbed by a displacement in the z-direction and then allowed to return to equilibrium, its equation of motion will be of the form

$$\frac{d^2 z}{dt^2} + 2\alpha \frac{dz}{dt} + \omega_0^2 z = 0 \tag{7.1}$$

where 2α is the damping factor and ω_0 its natural angular frequency. α is the conventional symbol for damping factor and should not be confused with polarizability. The solution is

$$z = z_0 e^{-\alpha t} \cos \omega_0' t \tag{7.2}$$

where
$$\omega_0' = (\omega_0^2 - \alpha^2)^{1/2}. \tag{7.3}$$

Since, normally, the damping is small, $\alpha^2 \ll \omega_0^2$ and $\omega_0' = \omega_0$ we may define a relaxation time for the oscillator as

$$\tau = \frac{1}{\alpha} \tag{7.4}$$

this being the time in which the amplitude of the oscillation falls to $1/e$ of its maximum value.

Now in the case of the polarization of a macroscopic dielectric by an applied alternating field, a phase shift will occur between the dipole oscillations and the field, due to the effects of the damping factor. The oscillations of the dipole will reach equilibrium in the same general manner as in the above case of equation (7.2). Fröhlich[20] therefore proposes a decay factor for the polarization, as was done for Debye relaxation in equation (6.2), of the form

$$\alpha(t) = \alpha(0) e^{-t/\tau} \cos(\omega_0 t + \psi) \tag{7.5}$$

where ψ is the phase angle by which the polarization lags the driving field. Substituting this in equation (6.1) gives

$$\epsilon_r(\omega) = \epsilon_\infty + \alpha(0) \int_0^\infty e^{-t/\tau} \cos(\omega_0 t + \psi) e^{j\omega t} dt$$

$$\therefore \quad \epsilon_r(\omega) - \epsilon_\infty = \frac{\alpha(0)\tau}{2} \left(\frac{e^{j\psi}}{1 - j(\omega_0 + \omega)\tau} + \frac{e^{-j\psi}}{1 + j(\omega_0 - \omega)\tau} \right)$$

$$= \frac{\alpha(0)\tau}{2} \cos\psi \left(\frac{1 + j\tan\psi}{1 - j(\omega_0 + \omega)\tau} + \frac{1 - j\tan\psi}{1 + j(\omega_0 - \omega)\tau} \right). \tag{7.6}$$

In order to find the constants $\alpha(0)$ and ψ we consider the limits of the equation. For $\omega \ll \omega_0$ ϵ_r will tend to a constant value. Let this be

$$\epsilon_r = \epsilon_\infty + \Delta\epsilon \tag{7.7}$$

where $\Delta\epsilon$ is real and will represent the excursion of ϵ' in passing through resonance from low to high values of frequency. Using (7.7) in (7.6), neglecting ω compared with ω_0, we get

$$\epsilon = \alpha(0)\tau \frac{\cos\psi(1-\omega_0\tau\tan\psi)}{1+\omega_0^2\tau^2}. \tag{7.8}$$

At very high frequencies ($\omega \gg \omega_0$) (7.6) simplifies to

$$\epsilon_r - \epsilon_\infty = \alpha(0)\tau \frac{\cos\psi}{1-j\omega\tau}. \tag{7.9}$$

But at very high driving frequencies the dipole oscillations will not be able to follow the variations of the applied field at all, and we drop back to relaxation conditions with an exponential decay factor. Equation (6.7) will then apply, i.e.

$$\epsilon_r - \epsilon_\infty = \frac{\epsilon_s - \epsilon_\infty}{1-j\omega t}.$$

Now $\epsilon_s - \epsilon_\infty$ is precisely the quantity $\Delta\epsilon$, so that

$$\epsilon_r - \epsilon_\infty = \frac{\Delta\epsilon}{1-j\omega\tau}. \tag{7.10}$$

From (7.9) and (7.10)

$$\Delta\epsilon = \alpha(0)\tau\cos\psi. \tag{7.11}$$

Substituting in (7.8) gives

$$\omega_0\tau = -\tan\psi. \tag{7.12}$$

Using (7.12) and (7.11) in (7.6) gives

$$\epsilon_r - \epsilon_\infty = \frac{\Delta\epsilon}{2}\left(\frac{1-j\omega_0\tau}{1-j(\omega_0+\omega)\tau} + \frac{1+j\omega_0\tau}{1+j(\omega_0-\omega)\tau}\right). \tag{7.13}$$

Separating real and imaginary parts gives

$$\epsilon' - \epsilon_\infty = \frac{\Delta\epsilon}{2}\left(\frac{1+\omega_0(\omega+\omega_0)\tau^2}{1+(\omega+\omega_0)^2\tau^2} + \frac{1-\omega_0(\omega-\omega_0)\tau^2}{1+(\omega-\omega_0)^2\tau^2}\right) \tag{7.14}$$

and

$$\epsilon'' = \frac{\Delta\epsilon}{2}\left(\frac{\omega\tau}{1+(\omega+\omega_0)^2\tau^2} + \frac{\omega\tau}{1+(\omega-\omega_0)^2\tau^2}\right). \tag{7.15}$$

These equations describe the real and imaginary parts of relative permittivity, as functions of frequency, for the case of resonance absorption. We first consider the influence of the parameter $\omega_0 \tau$. For $\omega_0 \tau \ll 1$ (7.13) reduces to

$$\epsilon_r - \epsilon_\infty = \frac{\Delta\epsilon}{2}\left(\frac{1}{1-j\omega\tau}+\frac{1}{1-j\omega\tau}\right)$$

$$= \frac{\Delta\epsilon}{1-j\omega\tau} \tag{7.16}$$

which is simply the case of Debye relaxation and is not of interest in the present instance.

For $\omega_0 \tau \gg 1$, taking $\omega \doteqdot \omega_0$ and $(\omega - \omega_0) = \pm\Delta\omega$, (7.14) becomes

$$\epsilon' - \epsilon_\infty \doteqdot \frac{\Delta\epsilon}{2}\left(\frac{3+(\Delta\omega)^2\tau^2-2\omega_0(\pm\Delta\omega)\tau^2}{2(1+(\Delta\omega)^2\tau^2)}\right). \tag{7.17}$$

If we assume that $\Delta\omega$ is finite and that the relaxation time τ is comparatively long (to be justified later), this may further be approximated to

$$\epsilon' - \epsilon_\infty = \pm\frac{\Delta\epsilon}{2}\left(\frac{\omega_0\Delta\omega}{\frac{1}{\tau^2}+(\Delta\omega)^2}\right). \tag{7.18}$$

By similar methods (7.15) reduces to

$$\epsilon'' = \frac{\Delta\epsilon}{2}\frac{\omega_0 1/\tau}{\frac{1}{\tau^2}+(\Delta\omega)^2}. \tag{7.19}$$

At the resonance frequency ω_0, $\Delta\omega = 0$ and $\epsilon' - \epsilon_\infty = 0$, from (7.18). The value of ϵ'' is a maximum at resonance and is given from (7.19) by

$$\epsilon''_{max} = \frac{\Delta\epsilon}{2}\omega_0\tau. \tag{7.20}$$

The half-value points, where ϵ'' falls to $1/2$ of its maximum value, correspond to $\pm\Delta\omega = 1/\tau$. Thus it is seen that, the longer the relaxation time τ, the sharper the resonance. Such a result is, of course, to be expected in view of (7.4) from which it is seen that a large relaxation time corresponds to small damping of the oscillator.

The maximum and minimum values of ϵ' are found by differentiating (7.18) with respect to $\Delta\omega$ and equating to zero. This gives $\Delta\omega = \pm 1/\tau$, substituting of which in (7.17) gives

$$\epsilon'_{max} = \epsilon_\infty + \frac{\Delta\epsilon}{4}\omega_0\tau \tag{7.21}$$

and

$$\epsilon'_{min} = \epsilon_\infty - \frac{\Delta\epsilon}{4}\omega_0\tau. \tag{7.22}$$

Equations (7.18) and (7.19) are plotted, as function of frequency, in Fig. 22.

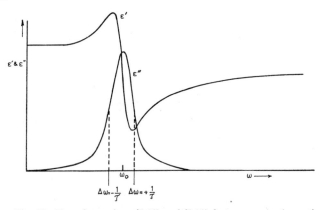

Fig. 22. Plot of equations (7·18) and (7·19) for resonance absorption

In Chapter 3 the equivalent resonant circuit was discussed. Making the approximations $\omega \doteq \omega_0$, equations (3.23) and (3.24) may be put in the form

$$(\epsilon')_{equiv} = \frac{1}{2\omega_0^2 LC_0}\frac{\omega_0\Delta\omega}{\left(\dfrac{R}{2L}\right)^2 + (\Delta\omega)^2} \tag{7.23}$$

7

and
$$(\epsilon'')_{\text{equiv}} = \frac{1}{2\omega_0^2 C_0 L} \frac{\omega_0 \dfrac{R}{2L}}{\left(\dfrac{R}{2L}\right)^2 + (\varDelta\omega)^2}. \tag{7.24}$$

Comparing (7.23) and (7.24) with (7.18) and (7.19) we find the relations

$$\tau = \frac{2L}{R} \tag{7.25}$$

and
$$\varDelta\omega = \frac{1}{\omega_0^2 C_0 L}. \tag{7.26}$$

It will be noted that (7.23) and (7.18) differ by the constant factor ϵ_∞ when (7.25) and (7.26) are used. This was mentioned in Chapter 3, when it was pointed out that resonance behaviour was, in practice, superimposed on a steady background value. No difficulty is involved here, since $\varDelta\epsilon$ was defined as that part of the total relative permittivity which undergoes the resonant excursion. If we substitute

$$\omega_0 L = \frac{1}{\omega_0 C} = \frac{1}{\omega_0(\epsilon')_{\text{equiv}} C_0}$$

in (7.26) we obtain $\varDelta\epsilon = (\epsilon')_{\text{equiv}}$. Equation (7.25) identifies the relaxation time τ with the well-known decay factor $2L/R$ for the series resonant circuit.

The nature of the damping forces on the oscillator must now be considered further. In the absence of coupling between adjacent oscillators, the principal damping will arise from radiation of electromagnetic energy by the oscillating charges. From the classical theory of electromagnetic radiation, the damping on an oscillating electron due to radiation is given by a damping factor

$$2\alpha \doteqdot \frac{\mu_0 e^2 \omega_0^2}{6\pi mc} \tag{7.27}$$

where ω_0 is the resonance frequency for small damping and c is the velocity of light. Substituting values we find

$$2\alpha \doteqdot 5 \times 10^{-24} \omega_0^2. \tag{7.28}$$

Experimentally electronic resonance absorption and emission are found in the visible region of light. The sodium D lines, at a wavelength of 5893 Å, correspond to $\omega_0 \doteq 3 \times 10^{15}$ so that $2\alpha \doteq 45 \times 10^6$ and the relaxation time τ is of the order of 5×10^{-9} sec. In terms of the period of oscillation of the electrons, which is of the order of 2×10^{-15} sec, this is a relatively long relaxation time. Substitution of these values into equation (7.17) justifies the assumptions made in its approximation. The variation of the refractive index of sodium vapour in the vicinity of the D lines provides good experimental confirmation of the dispersion formula. Below the frequency of the lines the refractive index is 1·005 and well above is 0·995. Thus $n^2 = \epsilon' = 1.01$ below and 0.99 above so that $\Delta\epsilon = 2 \times 10^{-2}$. The centre frequency of the lines corresponds to $\omega_0 = 3.08 \times 10^{15}$ rad/sec. If we ignore damping ($\tau = 0$) it is possible to plot the variation of ($\epsilon' - \epsilon_\infty$) in the vicinity of the two lines, D_1 at 5.088×10^{14} c/s (5896 Å) and D_2 at 5.093×10^{14} c/s (5890 Å), from equation (7.18). This is done in Fig. 23 and if it is compared with a spectroscopic photograph it will be found to coincide exactly over the plotted parts of the curve with the two lines, when they are photographed at high resolution.

The above derivation, it will be noted, is based on the assumption of classical mechanics that the oscillations may be of any energy and are not quantized. The Kramers[21] dispersion formula of quantum mechanics yields expressions for permittivity of precisely the same form as those above. The quantum mechanical and classical expressions become identical if the charge, e, and mass, m, of the oscillator are replaced by an effective charge e_i and effective mass m_i where these are not necessarily equal to the electronic charge and mass. The Kramers derivation shows that e_i and m_i may be defined by

$$\frac{e_i^2}{m_i} = 2 . \frac{\omega(l';l) \, [\mu(l;l')]^2}{h} \qquad (7.29)$$

where $\omega(l',l)$ is the frequency of oscillation of an electron between quantum states l' and l, and $\mu(l;l')$ is the induced moment due to shift of the electron from the state l to the state l'.

In the case of atomic polarization, the absorption due to resonance of the vibrating atoms (or more correctly the nuclei of these atoms)

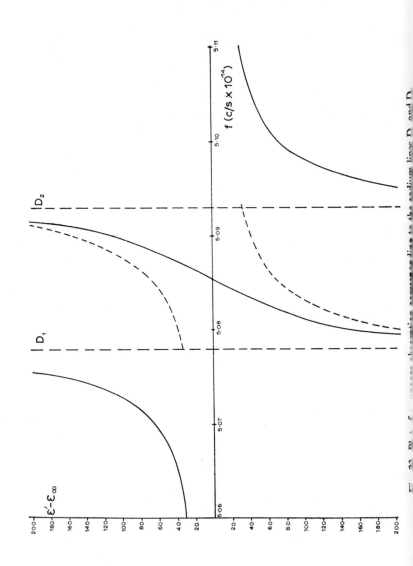

Fig. 3.9. Plot of ε' versus f corresponding to the sodium lines D_1 and D_2

lies in the infra-red band. This is to be expected since the atomic masses are much greater than the mass of the electron and their natural frequencies of oscillation would be lower. The classical dispersion expression also applies in this case with a value of m_i given by $m_1 m_2/(m_1 + m_2)$, where m_1 and m_2 are the masses of the atoms comprising the diatomic molecule. The effective charge, e_i, is defined as the rate of change, $d\mu/dr$, of the electric moment with inter-nuclear distance r.

Experimental Results

(a) Non-polar materials

For non-polar dielectrics, which class includes all pure elements whether solid, liquid or gas, the polarization is entirely electronic. However, some polar materials exhibit principally electronic polarization when they are of a highly symmetrical structure, like carbon tetrachloride. The test of whether or not the polarizability is due to displacement of the electrons is the Maxwell relation $\epsilon' = n^2$. Table I, given by Hartshorn and Saxton[22] makes the comparison between ϵ' and n^2 for a number of nominally non-polar materials.

Table I

MATERIAL	n^2	ϵ'	Frequency of measurement of ϵ' (Mc/s)
Hydrogen (liquid, $-253°$ C)	1·232	1·228	
Diamond	5·66	5·68	
Nitrogen (liquid, $-197°$ C)	1·453	1·454	
Oxygen (liquid, $-190°$ C)	1·491	1·507	
Chlorine (liquid)	1·918	1·910	
Bromine	2·66	3·09	
Paraffin (liquid)	2·19	2·20	10^3
Benzene	2·25	2·284	10^3
Polystyrene	2·53	2·55	10^2 to 10^{10}
Polyethylene	2·28	2·30	10^2 to 10^{10}
Carbon tetrachloride	2·13	2·238	
P.T.F.E.	1·89	2·10	10^2 to 10^9

Where the discrepancy between n^2 and ϵ' is larger than experimental error, as for instance with P.T.F.E., the difference is a measure of the atomic polarizability. The measured value of ϵ' is temperature-independent.

(b) Polar materials

Dielectrics exhibiting principally atomic polarizability comprise atoms of different kinds which are 'frozen-in' and are not free to change their equilibrium positions. These are the polar dielectric materials, characterized by a strong infra-red absorption. ϵ' may be expected to differ markedly from n^2 where atomic polarization is the dominating factor, and Table II, also due to Hartshorn and Saxton, gives some typical results.

Table II

MATERIAL	Temperature (°C)	n^2	ϵ'	$\tan \delta$	Frequency (c/s)
Sodium chloride	25	2·25	5·90	0·0001	10^2 to 10^6
Lithium fluoride		1·92	9·3		
Fluorite		2·06	6·8		
Mica	20		6·9	0.0001	10^3 to 10^8
	100		6·9		
Titanium dioxide	20	6·8	96	0.0004	10^3 to 10^8
	80		87	0·0004	10^8
Fused quartz	20	2·13	3·85	0·0001	10^4
	100		3·85	0·0001	10^3 to 10^8
Glass, soda-lime	20	2·30	7·60	0·010	10^6
Glass, borosilicate	20	2·28	4·79	0·0006	10^6

Interfacial Polarization

In Chapter 4 it was mentioned that a component, α_i, of polarizability arises from migration of charge carriers through the dielectric. The mechanism here differs totally from those so far discussed. Charges, such as electrons, are visualized as accumulating in the region of a discontinuity in the dielectric, and the simplest model for calculation is the Maxwell-Wagner two-layer condenser.

Two plane electrodes, of equal area, A, have, inserted between them, two parallel sheets of dielectric material. Let the sheets have relative permittivities ϵ_1' and ϵ_2', dielectric conductivities σ_1 and σ_2, and thicknesses d_1 and d_2 respectively. When a field is applied suddenly the flux density must be continuous across the dielectric interface, so that $D_1 = D_2$. Thus the fields across the dielectric slabs must be such that

$$\epsilon_1' E_1 = \epsilon_2' E_2. \tag{7.30}$$

When the condenser is fully charged a steady current will flow, due to the dielectric conductivity, which must be the same through each dielectric, i.e. $J_1 = J_2$ where J is current density in the dielectric material. It follows from Ohm's law, that

$$\sigma_1 E_1 = \sigma_2 E_2. \tag{7.31}$$

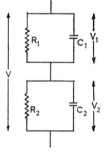

The equivalent circuit of the condenser will be of the form shown in Fig. 24. The applied voltage V, which is a constant, will always be given by

$$V = V_1 + V_2. \tag{7.32}$$

Fig. 24. Equivalent circuit for the Maxwell-Wagner two-layer condenser

The condition of current continuity, (7.31), is represented in the equivalent circuit by

$$C_1 \frac{dV_1}{dt} + \frac{V_1}{R_1} = C_2 \frac{dV_2}{dt} + \frac{V_2}{R_2}. \tag{7.33}$$

Substituting from (7.32) we have

and
$$\left.\begin{array}{l} (C_1 + C_2) \dfrac{dV_1}{dt} + \dfrac{V_1}{R} = \dfrac{V}{R_1} \\[3mm] (C_1 + C_2) \dfrac{dV_2}{dt} + \dfrac{V_2}{R} = \dfrac{V}{R_2} \end{array}\right\} \tag{7.34}$$

where
$$R = \frac{R_1 R_2}{R_1 + R_2}.$$

Rearranging and integrating gives

$$\frac{t}{CR} = -\log\left(\frac{V}{R_2} - \frac{V_1}{R}\right) + \text{const} \tag{7.35}$$

and a similar equation for V_2. The initial conditions are that V is applied at $t = 0$, at which time the voltage will be distributed between condensers in the inverse ratio of their fractional capacitances, i.e.

$$V_1 = V.\frac{C_2}{C_1 + C_2} \quad \text{and} \quad V_2 = V.\frac{C_1}{C_1 + C_2}.$$

Using this in (7.35) leads to

$$V_1 = V.\frac{R_1}{R_1 + R_2}\left(1 - \frac{(1 - C_2 R_2)}{\tau}e^{-t/\tau}\right)$$

and similarly

$$V_2 = V.\frac{R_2}{R_1 + R_2}\left(1 - \frac{(1 - C_1 R_1)}{\tau}e^{-t/\tau}\right) \tag{7.36}$$

where
$$\tau = CR = (C_1 + C_2).\frac{R_1 R_2}{R_1 + R_2} \tag{7.37}$$

and is the time constant of the complete circuit. It may be expressed in terms of the individual time-constants $\tau_1 = C_1 R_1$ and $\tau_2 = C_2 R_2$ as

$$\tau = \frac{R_2 \tau_1 + R_1 \tau_2}{R_1 + R_2} \tag{7.38}$$

We may use the equivalent circuit to obtain the frequency-dependence of permittivity, as follows:

$$Y = \frac{Y_1 Y_2}{Y_1 + Y_2}$$

$$= \frac{\left(\dfrac{1}{R_1} + j\omega C_1\right)\left(\dfrac{1}{R_2} + j\omega C_2\right)}{\dfrac{1}{R_1} + \dfrac{1}{R_2} + j\omega(C_1 + C_2)} \tag{7.39}$$

$$= \frac{(1 + j\omega\tau_1)(1 + j\omega\tau_2)}{R_1 + R_2 + j\omega(C_1 + C_2)R_1 R_2}$$

$$= \frac{1}{R_1 + R_2} \frac{(1 + j\omega\tau_1)(1 + j\omega\tau_2)}{1 + j\omega\tau}$$

$$= \frac{1}{R_1 + R_2}$$

$$\times \left(\frac{1 - \omega^2\tau_1\tau_2 + \omega^2\tau(\tau_1 + \tau_2) - j\omega\tau(1 - \omega^2\tau_1\tau_2) + j\omega(\tau_1 + \tau_2)}{1 + \omega^2\tau^2}\right). \tag{7.40}$$

By definition the admittance of an equivalent condenser is given from equation (1.32) as

$$Y = j\omega(\epsilon' - j\epsilon'')C_0 \tag{7.41}$$

where

$$C_0 = \frac{A}{d_1 + d_2}. \tag{7.42}$$

Thus equating (7.41) and (7.40)

$$\epsilon' = \frac{1}{C_0(R_1 + R_2)} \cdot \frac{\tau_1 + \tau_2 - \tau + \omega^2\tau_1\tau_2\tau}{1 + \omega^2\tau^2}. \tag{7.43}$$

At $\omega = 0$,

$$\epsilon' = \epsilon_s = \frac{\tau_1 + \tau_2 - \tau}{C_0(R_1 + R_2)} \tag{7.44}$$

and at $\omega = \infty$,

$$\epsilon' = \epsilon_\infty = \frac{\tau_1\tau_2}{\tau} \cdot \frac{1}{C_0(R_1 + R_2)}. \tag{7.45}$$

Substituting in (7.43) we have

$$\epsilon' = \epsilon_\infty + \frac{\epsilon_s - \epsilon_\infty}{1 + \omega^2 \tau^2}. \tag{7.46}$$

Comparing (7.46) with (6.8) it will be seen that the variation of ϵ' is precisely the same as that for the case of Debye relaxation, and τ may be identified with the relaxation time. Thus by measurement of the real part of relative permittivity it is not possible to distinguish between the effects of interfacial and orientational polarizability.

From (7.41) and (7.40) we also have

$$\epsilon'' = \frac{1}{\omega C_0 (R_1 + R_2)} \frac{1 - \omega^2 \tau_1 \tau_2 + \omega^2 \tau(\tau_1 + \tau_2)}{1 + \omega^2 \tau^2} \tag{7.47}$$

whence, using (7.44) and (7.45)

$$\epsilon'' = \frac{1}{\omega C_0 (R_1 + R_2)} + \frac{(\epsilon_s - \epsilon_\infty) \omega \tau}{1 + \omega^2 \tau^2}. \tag{7.48}$$

The second term of (7.48) is exactly the Debye relaxation equation (6.9), but there is an additional term inversely proportional to frequency. This means that the losses, represented by ϵ'', tend to infinity as ω tends to zero. Thus the case of interfacial polarizability may be distinguished from Debye relaxation by observing the variation of ϵ'' below the relaxation frequency. In the Debye case ϵ'' drops towards zero as the frequency is lowered.

It will be seen that the above calculation would be unaffected if the dielectric comprised a large number of thinner slabs, provided that there remained total thicknesses d_1 of the first and d_2 of the second. In the limit the slabs could be sheets of atoms and we will have made a smooth transition to the case of atomic distortional polarization, providing the latter were sufficiently damped to give a relaxation spectrum. If the geometric configuration were changed from slabs stacked in series to (say) particles of the one material embedded in a matrix of the other, the permittivity would still depend upon the ratio of the quantities of the two materials and would be independent of the sizes of the particles. However, the precise nature of the frequency-dependence of ϵ_r would depend on the shape and orientation of the particles. If the particles comprised several different dielectric materials, each type would be characterized by its own relaxation time and there would be a broad-band absorption. Further detail has been given by von Hippel[1] together with references to relevant published work.

CHAPTER 8

Dielectric Breakdown

Introduction

The failure of dielectrics under electric stress, generally referred to as breakdown, is a study of considerable practical importance. Under actual industrial conditions it is often found that the same material will exhibit a wide range of dielectric strengths, depending upon its environment and mode of use. However, even where the conditions of application and field distribution are apparently the same, breakdown is still found to spread over a wide range of applied stresses. Furthermore, this breakdown occurs generally at lower field strengths than those found for the pure material, measured under laboratory conditions.

In order to gain an understanding of the fundamental mechanisms of breakdown, it is necessary to resort to carefully controlled conditions in laboratory testing. Thus high field concentrations at the edges of electrodes must be avoided; the material under test must be pure and homogeneous and the atmosphere must be carefully controlled. Providing these precautions are taken, a number of basic mechanisms of breakdown can be distinguished. The first of these is termed *intrinsic breakdown*, which is electronic in nature, depending on the presence of electrons capable of migration through the lattice. The second is *thermal breakdown* which arises from the dielectric conductivity. Very generally, if a current is driven through the dielectric, by the application of a field, thermal breakdown arises when local heat is generated by this current faster than it can be dissipated. The temperature of the specimen rises and breakdown ensues as a result. The third mechanism, *discharge breakdown*, is not perhaps strictly a basic one, as it depends upon the presence of voids in the dielectric material.

There are other mechanisms which may be considered as basic, but are of a cumulative nature, gradually building up to breakdown. Of these the most important are electrochemical and chemical effects, due to which the insulant gradually deteriorates to a form having a higher conductivity. When this state is reached breakdown may occur by thermal effects, or by virtue of a lowered intrinsic strength, or by the formation of a discharge path (arc) between electrodes. Numbers of other possibilities have been proposed to explain effects observed in different practical cases. However, since the most widely met and fundamental mechanisms are intrinsic, thermal and discharge breakdown, detailed discussion will be confined to them.

Each of these types of breakdown will first be discussed with reference to solids. Liquids will be considered separately.

Intrinsic Breakdown

We consider a specimen of pure, homogeneous dielectric material, mounted between suitable electrodes so that a voltage can be applied across it, the circuit being arranged so that the current flowing can be measured. As the applied voltage is increased from zero a small current will begin to flow – often a small fraction of a microamp – which quickly levels off to a 'saturation' value. As the voltage continues to rise this current remains constant until a certain critical voltage, V_b, is reached. At this point the current suddenly rises rapidly to a high value; breakdown is said to have occurred and V_b is the breakdown voltage. In the case of intrinsic breakdown the current rises to the maximum value allowed by the supply in a time of the order of 10^{-8} sec. It is therefore postulated that the breakdown is electronic in nature. Fröhlich[23] proposed a model, based on this assumption, which will be described. However we must first consider the electronic structure of pure dielectrics.

Electrons in Insulators

The band theory of the electronic structure of solids has become common knowledge since the advent of the semiconductor, and the reader is assumed to be familiar with its general features.[24]

When atoms are brought together in a solid, the discrete energy levels permitted to the electrons in the free atom broaden into bands of permitted energies. At the absolute zero of temperature, in a perfect crystal having no defects, these bands are filled with electrons having energies up to some finite value. There may be permitted energy states above this value available to the electrons, but they will be empty. As the temperature rises from zero the electrons may acquire thermal energy and some of them will move up to higher energy levels, if they acquire just the right amount of energy to make the transition. In metals the bands of permitted energies are close together and many electrons are able to make such transitions.

The band of energies, which corresponds to electrons tied to the parent atoms, is referred to as the valence band. When the electrons make a transition of such energy that they escape from the parent atoms, the band to which they transfer is referred to as the conduction band. Once in the conduction band the electrons are free to migrate through the crystal.

In a metal the valence and conduction bands may overlap or, at most, be separated by a very small energy gap. In an insulator the two bands are separated by a large energy gap. This gap is so great that, at room temperature, the electrons cannot acquire sufficient thermal energy to make the transition to the conduction band. Thus they remain bound to the parent atoms and are unable to migrate through the crystal to give rise to electrical conduction.

On this picture the perfect dielectric crystal would be a perfect insulator with a dielectric conductivity of zero. In practice, however, all crystals must contain imperfections of one or more of the following types:

(i) *Vacancies and interstitials*

These may occur in crystals having no impurities and having stoichiometric (chemically correct) proportions. Vacancies are vacant lattice sites, i.e. points where atoms should be, but are missing. Interstitials are ions in positions between lattice points, i.e. displaced with respect to the regular array of atoms in the crystalline lattice.

(ii) *Non-stoichiometry*

In a crystal, which is not a pure element, it may very easily happen that there is a slight excess of one type of atom, with respect to the exact chemical proportions of the compound. The extra atoms may go into interstitial positions or the lattice may rearrange itself so that there are vacancies.

(iii) *Imperfections due to the presence of foreign atoms*

The effect of these imperfections is to change the charge distribution in the crystal. It can be shown that they act as local concentrations of charge which may trap electrons moving about in the crystal. In this way electrons are removed from the conduction band. Once trapped the electron occupies energy states similar to those available in an isolated atom, i.e. there is a ground state, with a number of excited

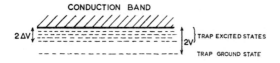

Fig. 25. Band structure of an insulator, showing trapping levels

levels available above it. Because of the effect of the surrounding medium, the separation of these levels is smaller than in the free atom. This may be seen from the fact that the ionization potential of an atom is inversely proportional to the square of the permittivity of the medium in which it is embedded. Thus if the relative permittivity of the dielectric medium were 10, the ionization potential of the impurity or interstitial atom will be 1/100 of its 'free' value. Now the valence band in the solid arises from, and corresponds in energy roughly to, the ground state of the free atom. Similarly the conduction band corresponds roughly to the ionized state of the free atom. In view of the much reduced ionization energy of the interstitial, it will be seen that the trapping levels should lie just below the conduction band, with the ground state well above the valence band. This situation is illustrated in Fig. 25.

In a crystal at low temperature most of the traps can be expected to be filled with electrons caught there as the crystal cooled down from the molten state from which it was prepared. At room temperature the thermal energy will be sufficient to eject electrons from the traps into the conduction band, because of the small energy gap between the trapping levels and the conduction band. Thus the crystal will always be expected to have some conduction (free) electrons, although the more perfect the crystal the smaller these will be in number.

Another defect of importance as a trapping mechanism is the grain boundary. This does not occur in a single crystal, as it is a surface over which there is a displacement of the regular crystal lattice, which can be described as the surface over which two single crystals of slightly different orientation meet. There will be considerable disturbance of the crystal field at this junction, and it may be expected to provide many trapping levels. A glassy material comprises an aggregation of a large number of microcrystals, and may be considered as the limiting case of a material with such defects.

Plastic materials which comprise a number of large molecules fitted together in a semi-random arrangement may also be expected to provide many trapping levels.

Electron Equilibrium

The electrons in the conduction band are free to move about the crystal, behaving as free electrons of effective mass m^*. Since there are relatively few of them, compared with the number of energy states available in the conduction band, they can be treated as if they were in an energy continuum. They will therefore reach a thermal equilibrium in accordance with classical, Boltzmann statistics. This means that the probability of an electron having an energy E is given by $e^{-E/kT}$, at a temperature T. The number of electrons per unit volume, n, with an energy between E and $E + dE$ will be given by

$$n = Ne^{-E/kT} \tag{8.1}$$

where N is the total number of electrons present in unit volume.

Equilibrium can only be established if the electrons undergo collisions. These may occur between electrons in the conduction band, between a conduction electron and a trapped electron and between a conduction electron and the lattice by virtue of the latter vibrating with thermal energy. In a very pure crystal the first two events are relatively rare, and the main scattering mechanism is electron-lattice interaction. For amorphous materials or pure crystals at high temperatures, the number of conduction and trapped electrons is much greater and the first two mechanisms predominate.

It is possible to define a critical temperature, T_c, below which only electron interaction with the lattice vibrations is important. The implication is that the more imperfect the crystal the lower will be the critical temperature.

Breakdown Mechanism

When a field is applied to the crystal, the conduction electrons will gain energy from it, and due to collisions between them this energy will be shared by all the electrons. Now if the crystal is in a stable condition this energy must be dissipated somehow, and if there are relatively few electrons this can only take place by its transfer to the crystal lattice. Such a transfer can only take place if the effective temperature, T, of the electrons is greater than T_0, the temperature of the lattice. The effect of the field, therefore, is first to raise the electron temperature and eventually, when thermal equilibrium is reached, to raise the temperature of the solid. For the case of the impure crystal, in which the electron interactions predominate, the field raises the energy of the electrons more rapidly than they can transfer energy to the lattice and the electron temperature will rise relative to that of the lattice. Because the most probable collisions are those between conduction and trapped electrons, the effect of increased electron temperature will be a rise in the number of trapped electrons reaching the conduction band. This increases the conductivity of the crystal and, as the electron temperature continues to increase, the stage of complete breakdown will eventually be reached. This will be called high-temperature breakdown.

In the pure crystal the electron-lattice interactions predominate. When no field is applied the electrons will be in equilibrium with the lattice having, for a given temperature, a most probable energy. If an electron acquires an energy greater than this value, it will quickly lose

8

it again to the lattice with a characteristic relaxation time $\tau(E)$, which is a function of energy. It can be shown that $\tau(E)$ is proportional to the square root of the electron energy, i.e. the higher the energy reached by the electron, the longer it takes to return to the most probable energy value. Thus the rate of loss of energy, $b(E)$, which is inversely proportional to relaxation time, is inversely proportional to the square root of energy, i.e. for any given electron of energy E

$$b(E) \propto \frac{1}{E^{1/2}} = \frac{A}{E^{1/2}} \qquad (8.2)$$

where A is a constant.

Now when a field is applied the electron gains energy from it. The rate at which energy is gained depends on how long the electron is accelerated by the field before undergoing a collision. The solid is more transparent to faster electrons and the relaxation time increases with increasing energy. Thus the rate of gain of energy $a(E)$, which is proportional to the relaxation time, increases with increasing energy and is, in fact, proportional to $E^{3/2}$. This rate also increases with increase of the applied field, F, and is, in fact, proportional to F^2, i.e.

$$a(E) \propto F^2 E^{3/2}. \qquad (8.3)$$

We can now distinguish three possible situations:

  (i) for small fields $a(E) < b(E)$, the electrons will, on average, lose energy until they reach the most probable value,
 (ii) for $a(E) = b(E)$ equilibrium conditions will obtain, corresponding to a maximum energy of electrons E_c, the critical energy,
(iii) for $a(E) > b(E)$ the electrons will steadily gain energy from the field.

Since $a(E)$ depends on field-strength F and $b(E)$ does not, the critical energy E_c will also depend upon field, decreasing in value as field increases, being, very roughly, inversely proportional to F.

We must now introduce a further consideration. When electrons reach a high enough energy, their collisions with the lattice will be capable of producing ionization of the atoms, injecting more electrons into the conduction band. This will rapidly lead to breakdown. The sequence of events in applying the field can now be considered; let the most probable electron energy, in the absence of a field, be E, critical energy E_c and ionization energy I.

(i) Very small field: $E \ll E_c > I$. Most electrons with energies in vicinity of E; some reaching higher energies by fluctuation may produce an occasional ionization but will decay back to energy E.

(ii) Moderate fields: $E < E_c \leqslant I$. A small number of electrons will reach energy E_c and then will continue to rise in energy until they reach I. Ionizations will take place, with increase in conductivity, but many products of the ionization process will have energies of less than E_c and will decay back to E. On balance there will be an increase in conductivity.

(iii) Higher fields: $I \gg E_c \geqslant E$. An increasing number of electrons will reach E_c and therefore be able to increase their energy to I. A larger number of ionizations take place whose products may still have energy greater than E_c. Conductivity will rise rapidly and 'avalanche' breakdown occurs. This will be called low-temperature breakdown.

It will be noted that a feature of this model is that it is not necessary for *all* the electrons to be raised to the ionization energy before breakdown occurs.

High-temperature Breakdown ($T > T_c$)

In this model the electronic temperature reaches an equilibrium value T, greater than the lattice temperature, at which the rate of gain of energy to the electrons exactly equals to rate of loss of energy from them to the lattice. For rates of gain of energy greater than this, the electron temperature 'runs away' and breakdown follows.

Fröhlich and Whitehead[25] have obtained expressions for these rates and define the critical field as that for which the rate of gain of energy equals the rate of loss.

This field is given by

$$F_c = C \exp\left(\frac{\Delta V}{2kT_0}\right) \tag{8.4}$$

where C is approximately a constant, T_0 is lattice temperature and

ΔV is the mean energy gap between the excited trapping levels and the bottom of the conduction band.

The electron temperature, T_m, at the critical field value is given by

$$\frac{1}{T_0} - \frac{1}{T_m} = \frac{k}{\Delta V}. \tag{8.5}$$

The dielectric conductivity, σ_m, at breakdown is given by

$$\sigma_m \doteqdot \sigma_0 \exp\left(\frac{V}{\Delta V} \cdot \frac{F^2}{F_c^2}\right) \tag{8.6}$$

where σ_0 is the conductivity in the absence of a field and F is the applied field.

Low-temperature Breakdown $(T > T_c)$

According to the model discussed above, breakdown will not occur until the critical energy, E_c, is less than, or equal to, the ionization energy, I. The lower limit to breakdown strength, i.e. the minimum field, F_c, at which breakdown will occur, is that given by the condition $E_c = I$.

Using the conditions previously discussed, this implies

$$a(I) = b(I)$$

where $\qquad b(I) = \dfrac{A}{I^{1/2}}, \quad$ from equation (8.2).

Now the rate of transfer of energy from field to electron will be given by equivalent current multiplied by field. If the average time between collisions is 2τ, the average velocity reached by an electron in the field will be $eF\tau/m^*$, corresponding to an electron current $e^2 F\tau/m^*$. Thus the rate of transfer of energy to the electron is given by

$$a(I) = \frac{e^2 \tau F_c^2}{m^*} \tag{8.7}$$

$$= b(I)$$

and $\qquad F_c = \left(\dfrac{m^* b(I)}{e^2 \tau}\right)^{1/2}. \tag{8.8}$

The feature of this result is that the temperature dependence of F_c is determined only by the temperature dependence of the relaxation time τ, which can be regarded as half the average time of flight of an electron between collisions. This quantity becomes smaller as the temperature increases so that we have the slightly surprising result that the breakdown field F_c will increase as the temperature rises. This rate of increase is, however, comparatively slow and experimentally F_c remains virtually constant over a wide range of temperature.

It is possible to calculate an expression for F_c in detail (see Whitehead, loc. cit.) and obtain the result

$$F_c = 1 \cdot 64 \times 10^7 \, V^{-1/3}(\epsilon_s - \epsilon) \, \lambda_0 \, \lambda^{-3/2}$$
$$\times \{1 + 2(e^{h\nu/kT} - 1)^{-1}\}^{1/2} \text{ volts/metre} \qquad (8.9)$$

where V is the molecular volume and $h\nu$ is the smallest amount of energy which can be transferred from electrons to lattice, or vice versa. λ is the residual wavelength in microns. This is the wavelength in the long infra-red region at which pronounced reflection takes place and is connected with the natural vibration frequency of the atoms of the crystal. λ_0 is in Ångstrom units and is the wavelength of the first maximum of the ultra-violet absorption spectrum. This result has been derived for relatively simple cases, such as alkali halide crystals. Fröhlich[20] has also made the calculations for more complicated crystals, but the general features of the result are the same.

Since the critical field value is dependent upon τ the effect of increasing the number of imperfections in the crystal can be foreseen. Obviously there will be an increasing probability of scattering as the number of imperfections increases and τ will be reduced, so that F_c increases with increasing concentration of imperfections or impurities.

Experimental Results
The foregoing theories make definite predictions, as regards dielectric breakdown, which may be tested experimentally.

Dealing first with the theory for a pure crystal the major qualitative features predicted are:

(1) There will be a critical temperature, T_c, below which dielectric strength increases slowly with increasing temperature, and above which the strength will decrease more rapidly with increasing temperature.

(2) Addition of foreign atoms to the crystal will increase the dielectric strength below T_c, but will not greatly affect it above.

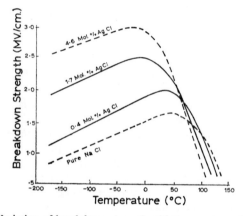

Fig. 26. Variation of breakdown strength with temperature, showing the effect of impurity atoms (after von Hippel and Lee[26])

(3) As the concentration of foreign atoms increases T_c will be lowered.

(4) Dielectric strength will decrease with increasing molecular volume.

Results obtained on NaCl crystals, with small percentages of added AgCl, by von Hippel and Lee[26] are given in Fig. 26. The predicted features 1, 2 and 3 are well confirmed. The dependence on molecular volume is illustrated in Fig. 27, which shows that breakdown strength decreases for ionic crystals in the sequence MF, M.Cl, MBr, MI, where M is a metal ion, the molecular radii increasing as one passes from fluorine to iodine through the halogens. These results are from the work of von Hippel[27] and of Vorob'ev[28].

In the case of amorphous solids the critical temperature will be very low, and the dielectric strength should decrease with increasing temperature over most of the range. This is well-illustrated by the results of von Hippel and Maurer[29], which compare the breakdown strength of crystalline quartz with that of fused (amorphous) quartz.

Fig. 27. Breakdown strength of various metal-halogen compounds, illustrating decrease of strength with increasing molecular volume (after von Hippel[27] and Vorob'ev[28])

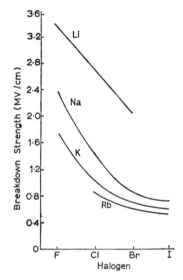

The results are given in Fig. 28 and it is seen that T_c for the amorphous material is below $0°$ C, whilst for the crystal it is above the measured temperature range.

Electric strengths calculated from equation (8.9) are compared with experimental results by Whitehead[25] for the alkali halides, and are reproduced below. It will be seen that good agreement is obtained.

Calderwood et al.[30] have shown the importance of freedom from mechanical stress in crystals tested. For KCl they found an average value of 0·93 Mv/cm in strain-free crystals, but this rose to an average of 1·24 Mv/cm when mechanical stress was applied. They suggest that many of the results quoted by Whitehead are higher by virtue of mechanical stress in the crystals tested.

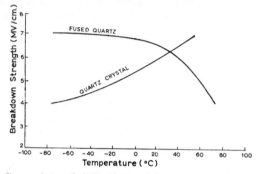

Fig. 28. Comparison of dielectric breakdown strength for crystal and amorphous solids (after von Hippel and Maurer[29])

Electric strengths in megavolts/centimetre

Crystal	NaCl	NaBr	NaI	KCl	KBr	KI	RbCl	RbBr	RbI
Experiment	1·5	1·0	0·8	0·93*	0·8	0·6	0·85†	0·6†	0·5
Theory	1·5	1·3	1·4	0·89	0·73	0·63	0·84	0·54	0·47

* Calderwood et al.[30].   † von Hippel[27].

Thermal Breakdown

The existence of current carriers in a dielectric implies that a conduction current will exist when a field is applied, and this will produce joule heating of the material. This is not the only source of heat, however. We have seen in previous chapters that dielectrics exhibit relaxation when an alternating field is applied. The relaxation means that there is some form of loss mechanism which, in turn, means that energy is transferred to the material from the field, and this energy will appear in the form of heat.

The principle of thermal breakdown is that heat is generated within the material faster than it can be conducted away. The resulting rise in temperature will reduce the intrinsic dielectric strength until breakdown occurs, or else melting or chemical decomposition of the material will occur before this point is reached.

The above considerations suggest that thermal breakdown strength will be lower for a.c. fields than for d.c. and that it will be lower for higher frequencies. This proves to be the case. In all experiments the cooling conditions, determining the rate at which heat is conducted away, will be of importance, and these must be standardized. In a thick slab, however, the rate at which cooling takes place is mainly determined by the thermal conductivity of the dielectric itself. On this basis an equation of thermal continuity can be set up, wherein the sum of the heat generated per second, due to the electric field and the heat lost by thermal conduction, must be zero for stability.

When the electrical conductivity, σ, is increased, the electrical heating for a given field increases and so the critical breakdown voltage decreases. If the thermal conductivity, k, increases, the heat gets away more quickly and the critical breakdown voltage will be higher. We may expect, therefore, that the ratio k/σ will appear in the expression for thermal breakdown voltage.

Whitehead[25] obtains for this voltage, the expression

$$V_m^2 = \int_{\theta_a}^{\theta_c} \left(\frac{8k}{\sigma}\right) d\theta \qquad (8.10)$$

where θ_a is the ambient temperature of the dielectric initially and θ_c is the temperature at which it decomposes or melts. σ is the a.c. or d.c. conductivity, and the precise result of the integration depends on the way in which σ varies with temperature. For the model used for conduction in the dielectric the temperature-dependence of conductivity can be shown to have the form

$$\sigma = \sigma_a \exp\left(\frac{\theta}{\theta_0}\right) \qquad (8.11)$$

where θ is the temperature rise above θ_a of the dielectric. θ_0 is the maximum possible temperature rise and σ_a is the conductivity at the ambient temperature. Using this in (8.10) gives

$$V_m^2 = q \frac{k\theta_0}{\sigma_a} \qquad (8.12)$$

assuming that k is independent of temperature, where q is a non-dimensional constant.

Maximum thermal voltages for a number of different materials are given in Table III, for a.c. fields at 50 c/s and an ambient temperature of 20° C. Some values of d.c. field are included.

Table III

MATERIAL	Max. thermal voltage in MV/cm	
	d.c.	a.c.
Crystals:		
Mica	24	7–18
Rock salt	38	1·4
Ceramics:		
H.F. Steatite	—	9·8
L.F. Steatite		1·5
High-grade porcelain	—	2·8
Borosilicate glass	—	4·8
Organic materials:		
Capacitor paper	—	3·5–4
Ebonite	—	1·45–2·75
Polythene	—	3–5
		(0·05 at 1 Mc/s)
Polystyrene	—	5
		(0·05 at 1 Mc/s)
Acrylic resins	—	0·3–1

The above-quoted results apply to a thick slab of dielectric, and are independent of its thickness. For thin specimens the maximum thermal voltage becomes thickness-dependent, and is proportional to the square root of the thickness, tending asymptotically to a constant value for thick specimens. When the specimen is stratified, however, consisting of alternate layers of conductor and insulator such as in the rolled capacitor, V_m becomes directly proportional to thickness. This is because the conducting layers are held at potentials such that the field strength in all the layers is the same, whereas in the solid dielectric, if a layer heats up so that its conductivity increases, the electric field automatically redistributes itself so that it is lower across the high-conductivity layer.

In practice, both industrially and under laboratory conditions, it is usually difficult to be sure that thermal breakdown has occurred. This is chiefly due to its onset being slow; for small percentage over-voltages breakdown may take days or weeks to appear, especially if the specific thermal resistance of the material is high. Once the temperature does start rising unstably it increases rapidly and breakdown occurs suddenly.

Discharge Breakdown

In practical insulators it is difficult to produce a block of dielectric which is a continuous, homogeneous solid. Usually there are voids in the material, containing gas, of varying shapes, sizes and volumes.

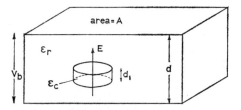

Fig. 29. Idealized cavity to illustrate discharge breakdown

The permittivity of the gas occluded in a cavity will generally be less than that of the surrounding dielectric medium so that, for a given electric stress E V/m in the material, the stress, E_c, in the cavity will be greater to an extent determined by the ratio of permittivity, and by the shape of the cavity.

The shape enters into consideration through the depolarizing factor which will be greatest for a flat, disc-shaped cavity whose axis of symmetry is parallel to the field direction. In such a case, assuming a depolarizing factor of 1,

$$E_c = \frac{\epsilon_r E}{\epsilon} \qquad (8.13)$$

where ϵ_r is the relative permittivity of the dielectric and ϵ_c of the gas in the cavity. If we assume that $\epsilon_c \doteq 1$, and that the breakdown stress for the gas is E_G V/m, we may calculate the voltage, V_b, across the whole dielectric for which a discharge will initiate in the cavity. If the dielectric slab is of thickness d and the disc-shaped cavity of thickness d_1, as shown in Fig. 29, we may treat them as capacitors in series. The capacitance of the dielectric is

$$C_d = \frac{\epsilon_r A \epsilon_0}{(d-d_1)} \qquad (8.14)$$

and of the cavity is

$$C_c = \frac{A \epsilon_0}{d_1} \qquad (8.15)$$

The voltage will divide between them in the inverse ratio of their capacitances so that, if V_b is the voltage across the dielectric, and $V_c = E_G d$, the voltage across the cavity is

$$V_c = \frac{C_d}{C_c + C_d} \cdot V_b \qquad (8.16)$$

and using (8.14) and (8.15)

$$V_c = \frac{V_b}{1 + \frac{1}{\epsilon_r}\left(\frac{d}{d_1} - 1\right)} \qquad (8.17)$$

i.e.

$$V_b = E_G d_1 \left\{ 1 + \frac{1}{\epsilon_r}\left(\frac{d}{d_1} - 1\right) \right\}. \qquad (8.18)$$

In practice a cavity in the material is more often nearly spherical. For such a case

$$E_c = \frac{3\epsilon_r E}{(\epsilon_c + 2\epsilon_r)} \doteq \frac{3E}{2} \quad \text{for } \epsilon_r \gg \epsilon_c. \qquad (8.19)$$

Hall and Russek[31] have shown that the electric strength of an air-filled spherical cavity of diameter d is approximately the same as the strength of an air-filled, parallel-plate condenser with the plates a distance d apart. On the basis of this an equivalent circuit for the cavity and dielectric such as that given in Fig. 30 may be used. C_c represents the cavity and C_d the column of dielectric, above and below it, which has the same diameter. C_b represents the surrounding dielectric. As the voltage V_b is increased from zero the stress across the cavity will increase until the voltage reaches the value given by (8.18) and the gas in the hole breaks down. The voltage across C_c will then fall, by virtue of neutralization of charge on the walls of the cavity, until it is low enough for the discharge to be extinguished. This takes place very rapidly, in a time of the order of 10^{-7} sec, and the voltage falls by a small amount ΔV_c. A corresponding drop in voltage will appear across C_b whose value will be determined by the

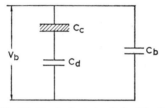

Fig. 30. Equivalent circuit for Fig. 29

loss of charge. The fall ΔV_c takes place across C_c and C_d whose total effective capacitance is $C_c C_d / C_c + C_d$. The loss of charge will be $\Delta V_c . (C_c C_d / C_c + C_d)$ and this will be made up by transfer of charge from C_b, with accompanying reduction ΔV_b in V_b. Thus

$$\Delta V_c . \frac{C_c C_d}{C_c + C_d} = C_b \Delta V_b. \qquad (8.20)$$

Usually $C_d \ll C_c$ because C_c is equivalent to a parallel-plate capacitor with very small spacing between the plates whilst for C_d the spacing is large. Thus (8.20) simplifies to

$$\Delta V_b = \frac{C_d}{C_b} . \Delta V_c. \qquad (8.21)$$

ΔV_b may be measured by incorporating the dielectric in a balanced Schering bridge and observing the instantaneous unbalance, which appears as an instantaneous increase in the capacitance of the specimen.

Measurements of this type combined with electro-photographs show that small discharges occur at many separate sites, each of area less than 0·3 mm diameter, and that there is almost complete charge neutralization over the small area, corresponding to $\Delta V_c \doteqdot V_c$.

When a steady voltage is applied to the specimen an initial discharge occurs, probably at the site of some imperfection or residual surface

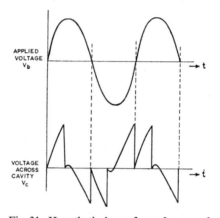

Fig. 31. Hypothetical waveforms for case of
discharge breakdown

charge, at a voltage possibly 10 to 20% below that predicted by equation (8.18). As the applied voltage rises this is followed by discharges at other sites, until the whole cavity is affected. With further increase in voltage new discharges occur at already partially discharges sites. If the voltage is maintained constant, however, further discharges can only occur by charge leakage through the material to re-charge the sites already discharged.

When an alternating voltage is applied discharges will occur during each half-cycle. If we suppose that the discharge occurs just at the crest of the first positive half-cycle, and that the area completely discharges, then, as the alternating voltage falls from its positive crest value a reverse field builds up across the cavity. This would cause a new discharge near the point where the alternating voltage crosses the zero axis. A further discharge would occur when the voltage reaches negative crest value and again as it passes through zero, as illustrated in Fig. 31. If the applied voltage were greater than the discharge inception voltage, several discharges should occur during each cycle. If, however, charge leakage over the surface of the inside of the cavity is fairly rapid, this behaviour will be modified, and there may be fewer discharges per cycle.

Electric Strength with Discharges

The process by which internal discharges may initiate breakdown depends, to a degree, on the material in which they occur. In polythene, which has been studied by Mason[32], the inside surface of the cavity is initially eroded by the discharges. The rate of erosion increases rapidly with increase of electric stress beyond the discharge inception value, the discharges becoming more concentrated and forming deeper pits. This erosion is probably thermal, since it may be shown that the energy liberated by the discharge could instantaneously raise the surface of the cavity by several hundred degrees. As the discharges continue the pits attain a critical length, after which fine channels propagate from them through the remaining material, causing failure. The mechanism is that the energy liberated increases with the length of channel over which the discharge occurs. Thus the critical depth of pit is reached when the liberated energy is sufficient to promote rapid destruction of the material. The fineness of the channel is accounted for by the high electric stress which will exist around the fine tip of the breakdown channel. The stress can easily reach the intrinsic breakdown value at the top of a very fine channel.

Sometimes the heat liberated by the discharge is sufficient to carbonize the channel, short-circuiting it and preventing further breakdowns. This is more likely to happen in wax-impregnated paper insulation than in plastics.

A review article on dielectric breakdown in solids has been published by Mason[33].

Breakdown in Liquids

Pure non-polar dielectric liquids, such as paraffins, have resistivities as high as 10^{18} Ω-cm and breakdown strengths of the order of 10^6 V/cm. In low fields the conduction current is extremely small and has been shown to be largely due to current carriers arising from ionization of atoms by ambient radiation, such as cosmic rays. Other contributions to conductivity come from ionized impurities in the liquid, and from the electrodes.

The earlier theories of breakdown in liquids have all assumed that it occurs by avalanche ionization of the atoms, induced by conduction electrons accelerated in the applied field. The source of these electrons is assumed to be the cathode electrode, from which they may be emitted by field effect or by Schottky effect. In field emission the electrons escape from the cathode by tunnelling through the surface barrier, aided by the applied field. These are accelerated by the field and produce ionization. The resulting positive ions form a positive space-charge near the surface of the cathode, increasing the field emission until it reaches catastrophic proportions. Schottky emission is thermionic emission from the cathode, aided by lowering of the cathode work function by the applied field. This emission would obey Richardson's equation and the conduction current would be a function of temperature. Such is the case for field strengths below the breakdown value; however, the breakdown strength itself is found to be fairly constant over a wide range of temperatures. This is taken to be evidence that the catastrophic increase in emission from the cathode, which would correspond to breakdown, comes mainly through field emission.

Once liberated from the cathode an electron gains energy from the applied field. In the electronic theory of breakdown it is assumed that, in a sufficiently high field, the electron will gain more energy than it loses in vibrational collisions with the atoms, in the same way as was discussed for high-temperature intrinsic strength in solids. These electrons are accelerated until they gain sufficient energy to ionize the liquid molecules and initiate an electron avalanche. Lewis[34] has discussed this model in detail and concludes that vibrational collisions account for the major energy loss in the hydrocarbons, the carbon-hydrogen bond vibrations being the main absorbent.

The applied field, at which an avalanche can initiate, is given by equating the energy gained by an electron from the field in travelling over its mean free path to that required for ionization of the molecule, i.e.

$$e . E . \lambda = ch\nu \qquad (8.22)$$

where $h\nu$ is the ionization quantum for the liquid molecule, and λ the mean free path of the electron.

This theory satisfactorily predicts the order of magnitude of the breakdown strengths of hydrocarbons. It does not, however, very easily account for the time-lag observed between the application of a pulse of voltage greater than the breakdown value and the actual onset of breakdown, which is of the order of one microsecond. The reasons for this have not yet been resolved; one of the most difficult features for which to account in terms of electronic mechanisms, however, is the strong dependence of liquid breakdown strength upon applied hydrostatic pressure. To meet this the cavitation theory of breakdown has been formulated, which is the parallel in liquids to discharge breakdown in solids.

Kao[35] has shown that the presence of bubbles in a liquid dielectric could lead to breakdown, and has worked out an appropriate mathematical model. It seems probable that bubbles can be formed by one, or more, of the following mechanisms:

(a) gas pockets on the electrode surface,
(b) electrostatic repulsion between space charges – positive ionic in the cathode region and negative in the body of liquid. This force may be sufficient to overcome the surface tension of the liquid, when bubbles could form,
(c) gaseous products of ionization of the molecules by energetic electrons,
(d) vaporization of liquid by corona-type discharge from points and asperities on the electrodes.

If a spherical bubble forms, it will rapidly elongate in the direction of the field, to minimize its potential energy in the field. This has the effect of increasing the voltage drop along the bubble. Kao has calculated the breakdown field strength in terms of surface tension σ,

9

initial radius r, voltage drop V_b, and relative permittivities. He gives the field strength for breakdown as

$$E_0 = \frac{1}{\epsilon_1 - \epsilon_2} \left\{ \frac{24\pi\sigma(2\epsilon_1 + \epsilon_2)}{r} \left[\frac{\pi}{4\sqrt{}} \middle/ \left(\frac{V_b}{2rE_0} \right) - 1 \right] \right\}^{1/2} \quad (8.23)$$

where ϵ_1 and ϵ_2 are the relative permittivities of the dielectric and of the bubble respectively. When the pressure is increased the radius, r,

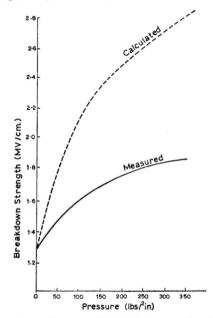

Fig. 32. Theoretical and measured breakdown strengths of *n*-hexane as a function of pressure (after Kao[35])

of the bubble will decrease and the breakdown strength will increase. A comparison of the theoretical and experimental curves is given in Fig. 32 for *n*-hexane. It will be seen that the general features of the experimental results are accounted for, but that the magnitudes are in poor agreement. A review of this and other mechanisms has been given by Sharbaugh and Watson[36].

CHAPTER 9

Piezoelectricity and Ferroelectricity

Introduction

In earlier chapters we have seen that dielectric theory predicts the possibility of spontaneous polarization. This is found to occur in highly specialized classes of crystal having a low symmetry, and for an understanding of the fundamental mechanism it is necessary to know the crystal structure. The occurrence of spontaneous polarization is associated with the phenomenon of pyroelectricity, which results from the temperature-dependence of the polarization. In some dielectric crystals it is found that mechanical strain may produce an electrostatic charge on the faces of a crystal, this being known as piezoelectricity. It is the purpose of this chapter to discuss the fundamental mechanisms of these effects and to give the principal experimental observations. Devices based on them will be dealt with in Chapter 10.

The Piezoelectric Effect

Piezo is derived from the Greek word meaning 'to press', and the piezoelectric effect is the production of electricity by pressure. It occurs only in insulating materials and is manifested by the appearance of charges on the surfaces of a single crystal when it is mechanically deformed. It is easy to see the nature of the basic molecular mechanism involved. The application of stress has the effect of separating the centre of gravity of the positive charges from the centre of gravity of the negative charges, producing a dipole moment. Clearly whether or not the effect occurs will depend upon the symmetry of the distributions of the positive and negative ions. This restricts the effect so that it can occur only in those crystals not having a centre of symmetry, since, for a centro-symmetrical crystal, no combination of uniform stresses will produce the necessary separation of the centres of gravity of the charges. This description makes it clear that the converse piezoelectric effect must exist. When

121

an electric field is applied to a piezoelectric crystal it will strain mechanically. There is a one-to-one correspondence between the piezoelectric effect and its converse, in that crystals for which strain produces an electric field across them will strain when an electric field is applied. Electrostriction is a property of all dielectrics, not restricted to piezoelectric materials, and is the production of mechanical strain in the crystal, by the application of an electric field, arising from distortion or displacement of molecules or atoms. It is generally a much weaker phenomenon than the piezoelectric effect except in ferroelectric crystals which will be dealt with later. It is particularly distinguished from the piezoelectric effect by virtue of being an even function of the applied field, i.e. reversal of the sign of the field does not reverse the direction of strain. It is therefore described as a second-order effect. In the piezoelectric effect, on the other hand, the field produced is proportional to the strain and reverses when the sign of the strain is reversed. This is a first-order effect.

The pyroelectric effect, as the name implies, is connected with heat. Certain crystals, such as tourmaline, acquire an electric charge when heated and are termed pyroelectric. The fact that all pyroelectric crystals are piezoelectric as well leads to some difficulties; when heated, the crystal will expand and may be deformed. Because of the piezoelectric effect it will acquire an electric charge by virtue of the deformation. This may be termed the indirect pyroelectric effect; there is also a direct effect in which there is a change of positive and negative polarization on certain portions of the crystal simply due to the change of temperature produced by uniform heating. In experimental observations the direct and indirect effects are difficult to separate, and there would be little point in so doing since pyroelectric behaviour can be considered simply as a feature of piezoelectric crystals, and related to piezoelectricity, because all pyroelectric crystals are also piezoelectric.

Crystals can be divided into thirty-two classes on the basis of their symmetry. Of these, twenty possess the property of piezoelectricity by virtue of their low symmetry and of the twenty, ten are pyroelectric. It is necessary to outline the basis of crystal classification in order to consider the subject further.

Crystal Symmetry

Crystal classification is based on the unit cell, which is a simple parallelepiped out of which the crystal can be constructed. This means that if the unit cell is translated through a distance equal to the length of one of its sides, any one molecule in it finds itself in identical surroundings. The crystal lattice is an assembly of a large number of unit cells, and the way in which these are put together determines the macroscopic shape of the crystal.

Bravais showed that the number of types of polyhedron which could be fitted together to fill all space was seven. Each proposed shape is a crystal system so that each of Bravais' proposed polyhedra represents a possible unit cell. The seven crystal systems are named triclinic, monoclinic, orthorhombic, tetragonal, trigonal, hexagonal and cubic, in ascending order of symmetry. The systems are specified in terms of three crystallographic axes, a, b and c, by stating the lengths of the unit cell in each direction. The axes are not necessarily perpendicular to each other. Bravais realized that the condition that each point in the unit cell should find itself in the same environment on translation in the a, b or c directions would include body-centred and face-centred points. The inclusion of these puts up the number of basic shapes to fourteen, referred to as the Bravais' lattices, as illustrated in Fig. 33.

The location of the atoms within the unit cell provides a further sequence of patterns and, for each of the crystal systems, there is a variety of possible atomic arrangements. These can be specified by inserting points in the lattice, such that the pattern can be made to repeat itself by a combination of translation and rotation, or by reflection in a plane and translation. There are 230 of these arrangements possible in the seven crystal systems and they are called the space groups.

In general, the points forming the space groups do not necessarily represent the positions of the atoms, but rather define the unit cell within which the atoms are located. The space groups are divided into thirty-two point-groups, each possessing certain symmetry with respect to a point. These are the thirty-two crystal classes and are each designated by a symbol, indicating the rotations about an axis and reflections in a plane that constitute the symmetry operations of the group; these operations never include translation of the lattice as a whole.

The morphology (crystal structure) of a crystal determines its physical properties; this is a fundamental fact of crystal physics known as Neumann's principle. According to it, when the elements of symmetry characterizing the morphology of the crystal are known,

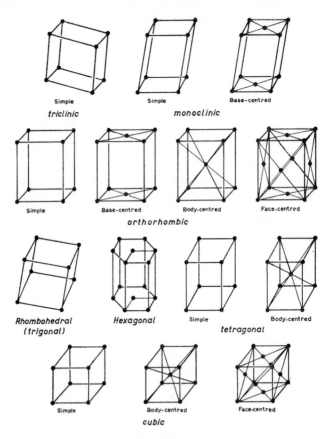

Fig. 33. The 14 Bravais lattices

the symmetry of its physical properties can be predicted. Any given physical property, such as thermal expansion, or the elastic constant, may be of higher symmetry than the crystal but cannot be of lower.

Study of the fourteen Bravais lattices immediately shows that most crystals can be expected to be anisotropic; i.e. to have different magnitudes for physical properties in different directions within the crystal. The greater the crystal symmetry the lower the anisotropy until, in the simple cubic crystal, one may expect isotropic behaviour. Now it can be seen that a crystal having a high degree of anisotropy may strain by different amounts along the different axes, when subjected to uniform hydrostatic pressure. Such differential straining could easily give rise to the separation of the centres of gravity of the positive and negative charges, and thus to an induced piezoelectric moment. We now discuss this anisotropic behaviour further.

Crystal Anisotropy

In an anisotropic material the electric field $\mathbf{E}$ will induce a polarization $\mathbf{P}$ which is not, in general, parallel to it. Thus the vector relations between $\mathbf{E}$, $\mathbf{P}$, and flux density $\mathbf{D}$ will no longer have a simple form but require equations specifying the components of each quantity along each of the x-, y- and z-axes. Using the subscripts 1 for x, 2 for y and 3 for z the equations are

$$\left.\begin{aligned}
\mathbf{P}_1 &= \chi_{11}\,\epsilon_0\,\mathbf{E}_1 + \chi_{12}\,\epsilon_0\,\mathbf{E}_2 + \chi_{13}\,\epsilon_0\,\mathbf{E}_3 \\
\mathbf{P}_2 &= \chi_{21}\,\epsilon_0\,\mathbf{E}_1 + \chi_{22}\,\epsilon_0\,\mathbf{E}_2 + \chi_{23}\,\epsilon_0\,\mathbf{E}_3 \\
\mathbf{P}_3 &= \chi_{31}\,\epsilon_0\,\mathbf{E}_1 + \chi_{32}\,\epsilon_0\,\mathbf{E}_2 + \chi_{33}\,\epsilon_0\,\mathbf{E}_3
\end{aligned}\right\} \tag{9.1}$$

and

$$\left.\begin{aligned}
\mathbf{D}_1 &= \epsilon_{11}\,\mathbf{E}_1 + \epsilon_{12}\,\mathbf{E}_2 + \epsilon_{13}\,\mathbf{E}_3 \\
\mathbf{D}_2 &= \epsilon_{21}\,\mathbf{E}_1 + \epsilon_{22}\,\mathbf{E}_2 + \epsilon_{23}\,\mathbf{E}_3 \\
\mathbf{D}_3 &= \epsilon_{31}\,\mathbf{E}_1 + \epsilon_{32}\,\mathbf{E}_2 + \epsilon_{33}\,\mathbf{E}_3
\end{aligned}\right\} \tag{9.2}$$

In (9.1) the susceptibility x_{ij} is proportional to the ratio of the polarization $\mathbf{P}_i$ in the i-direction to the component of the applied field $\mathbf{E}_j$ in the j-direction. Similarly in (9.2) the permittivity ϵ_{ij} is the ratio of the flux density $\mathbf{D}_i$ in the i-direction to the component of field $\mathbf{E}_j$ in the j-direction. The two are related by

$$\chi_{ij} = \frac{\epsilon_{ij}}{\epsilon_0} - 1. \tag{9.3}$$

This gives nine permittivities required to characterize the response of the crystal to an applied field. Actually it can be shown that we always have

$$\epsilon_{ij} = \epsilon_{ij}$$

and
$$\chi_{ij} = \chi_{ij} \tag{9.4}$$

so that the number of independent coefficients in each of (9.1) and (9.2) is only six.

In a similar way there will exist a set of equations relating the stress applied to a crystal to the strains along the three crystallographic axes produced by it. There are two types of strain which may be produced, namely linear strain along any one of three axes and shear strain resulting from torque around any one of three axes, giving six degrees of freedom. Either one of these components would be represented by a coefficient but the combination of them requires $6 \times 6 = 36$ coefficients. These are the elastic constants c_{ij}, for which the same type of relation as (9.4) can be shown to exist, so that the number of independent elastic constants is twenty-one.

Now the piezoelectric effect is an electro-mechanical one in which polarization $\mathbf{P}$ is related to mechanical stress T or, conversely, electric stress $\mathbf{E}$ is related to mechanical strain S.

These relations may be written as

$$\mathbf{P}_i = \sum_j d_{ij} T_j \quad (i = 1, 2, 3; j = 1, \ldots, 6) \tag{9.5}$$

and
$$S_j = \sum_i d_{ij} \mathbf{E}_i \quad (i = 1, 2, 3; j = 1, \ldots, 6) \tag{9.6}$$

where i represents the three degrees of freedom corresponding to the three crystal axes, j the six types of possible strain, and d_{ij} are the piezoelectric coefficients. There will be eighteen such components, but again, with the restriction $d_{ij} = d_{ji}$, this reduces to fifteen independent ones.

How many of the coefficients actually exist (i.e. are non-zero) depends upon the crystal symmetry. For example, in a centrosymmetrical system all the piezoelectric coefficients are zero. The introduction of any element of symmetry reflects in the electrical, mechanical and piezoelectric coefficients reducing the number of independent components. By suitably combining the matrix representing crystal symmetry with the matrix of the piezoelectric coefficients it is possible to predict whether or not a given crystal is capable of exhibiting piezoelectricity[37]. Whether or not the crystal actually does so, has to be determined experimentally, since the above classification is based only on symmetry considerations and takes no account of the actual charge distribution and polar configurations within the crystal.

From the molecular point of view a material exhibiting piezoelectricity must contain permanent dipole moments. Thus, to determine whether or not a crystal is piezoelectric, we may determine the distributions of the dipoles and consider their reactions to strain. This has been done in some detail by von Hippel[38] and it is sufficient here to say that, once the ionic distributions in the crystal lattice are known, it is possible to deduce, from the symmetry of the arrangements, which of the piezoelectric coefficients will be finite and which zero. Such considerations lead to the conclusion that the piezoelectric crystal must not only have a macroscopically asymmetric structure, but also that the molecular groups responsible for piezoelectricity should have no centre of symmetry.

Piezoelectric Crystals

The piezoelectric properties of a crystal will be completely specified when its piezoelectric coefficients and permittivities have been measured. We may illustrate methods of measurement by reference to experiments on quartz, one of the most widely used piezoelectric materials. Chemically, quartz is silicon dioxide (SiO_2) which crystallizes in the trigonal trapezohedral class. The axes are usually labelled x, y and z where the latter is an axis of three-fold symmetry. This is to say that the distribution of the molecules is such that rotation through $120°$ about the z-axis brings each into identical surroundings. This crystal structure is called the α-phase and is very

stable at room temperature; the melting point is 1750° C. Large
single crystals are found in nature, principally in Brazil, but as a
result of research during the 1950's, synthetic crystals of large size
and high purity can now be grown by the hydrothermal process, and
are replacing natural crystals for
many applications.

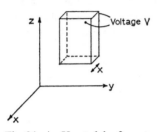

Fig. 34. An X-cut slab of quartz

Slabs may be cut from the crystal
with various orientations and,
where their sides are parallel to
the crystal axes, they are named by
the axis perpendicular to the face
of the slab. Jacques Curie used an
X-cut crystal for static measurements on piezoelectric behaviour,
as illustrated in Fig. 34.

Evaporated metal electrodes are applied to the large faces (yz
planes) and a voltage, V, is applied between
them, in the x-direction. This causes a change in
thickness δx. By definition the piezoelectric
coefficient is given by

$$d_{11} = \frac{\dfrac{\delta x}{x}}{\dfrac{V}{x}} = \frac{\delta x}{V}. \qquad (9.7)$$

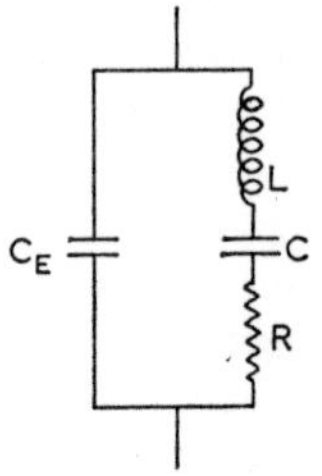

Whilst such an experiment is possible, accurate
determination of the constants is usually done
dynamically.

Fig. 35. Equiva-
lent circuit of an
oscillating crystal

Thus, if the applied field in the above experiment is an alternating
one, the crystal will alternately increase and decrease in thickness
and, if the field is of the right frequency, a mechanical resonance may
be induced. The electrical circuit equivalent to the oscillating crystal
is that given in Fig. 35.

The series LCR arm is equivalent to the crystal whilst C_E is the
capacitance of the electrodes. The equivalent inductance L is related
to the mass of the crystal, C to its mechanical compliance and R to
the frictional resistance to its mechanical vibrations. C_E is related

to the dielectric constant. By measuring the series and parallel resonant frequencies, the Q factor and the capacitance at low frequencies, all the circuit constants can be deduced and, from them, the dielectric, elastic and piezoelectric coefficients may be found. The relationships between the measured values and the constants depend upon the cut of crystal used and its mechanical mode of vibration. These have been worked out by Mason[37] who gives the following values for quartz:

$$d_{11} = -2 \cdot 25_3 \times 10^{-12} \text{ coulombs/newton or metres/volt}$$
$$d_{14} = 0 \cdot 85_3 \times 10^{-12} \text{ coulombs/newton or metres/volt}$$

other coefficients zero

and
$$\epsilon_1 = 4 \cdot 58$$
$$\epsilon_3 = 4 \cdot 70$$

where ϵ_1 is the relative permittivity in the x-direction, equal to that in the y-direction, and ϵ_3 is the relative permittivity in the z-direction.

So far only one type of piezoelectric constant, d_{ij}, has been defined, relating strain to applied field. In fact, referring back to equation (9.6), it is based on the converse piezoelectric effect, i.e. the production of strain by application of a field. In general, for a strain S and field E, the definition of d is

$$d = \frac{\partial S}{\partial E}. \tag{9.8}$$

Other constants can be defined in a similar way. If, instead of allowing the crystal to strain, it is prevented from altering its shape by clamping, the application of a field will produce a stress $\mathbf{T}$. We define a constant

$$e = \frac{\partial T}{\partial E}. \tag{9.9}$$

Similarly, if a stress T is applied to the crystal, a field E will appear across it, and another constant may be defined as

$$g = \frac{\partial E}{\partial T}. \tag{9.10}$$

If the stress is relieved by the crystal straining by an amount S, a fourth constant is

$$h = -\frac{\partial E}{\partial S}. \tag{9.11}$$

The units of these constants follow from their definitions and thus, since strain is a number (defined by $\delta l/l$), d should be in metres per volt and h in volts per metre. e will be newtons per volt-metre and g volt-metres per newton. However, the conventionally-used units are the following:

$$d = \text{coulombs/newton} \qquad h = \text{newton/coulomb}$$
$$e = \text{coulombs/metre}^2 \qquad g = \text{metre}^2/\text{coulomb}.$$

Conversion is effected by use of $Q = CV$ (coulombs = farads × volts) and

$$F = \frac{Q_1 Q_2}{\epsilon r^2} \left(\text{newtons} = \frac{\dfrac{\text{coulombs}^2}{\text{farads}}}{\text{metres}} . \text{metres}^2 \right).$$

The relation between the four constants are as follows:

$$d = \epsilon^T g_{\mathrm{E}} = eS^{\mathrm{E}}$$
$$e = dc^{\mathrm{E}} = \epsilon^S h$$
$$h = \beta^S e = gc^{\mathrm{D}}$$
$$g = hS^{\mathrm{D}} = \beta^{\mathrm{T}} d$$

where the superscripts refer to the parameter kept constant and are T = tensile stress, E = field, S = strain, D = dielectric flux density; s_{ij} are elastic compliances and c_{ij} elastic constants; β is the inverse of permittivity.

Piezoelectric Materials

Practical applications of piezoelectrics are dealt with in the next chapter. To complete the present discussion the more important current materials will be reviewed.

Rochelle Salt

This is one of the first piezoelectric materials to be recognized as such, by the Curies in 1880. Chemically, it is sodium potassium tartrate ($NaKC_4H_4O_6$—$4H_2O$) and crystallizes in the orthorhombic class. The crystalline form, however, undergoes phase changes such that the crystal is monoclinic in the range $-18°$ C to $23·7°$ C, and orthorhombic outside this range. In the monoclinic phase it is ferroelectric, i.e. it shows a spontaneous polarization.

In the orthorhombic form the crystal shows only shear piezoelectric constants, d_{14}, d_{25} and d_{36}, the remainder being zero. In the monoclinic form it has both linear and additional shear constants d_{14}, d_{16}, d_{27}, d_{22}, d_{23}, d_{25}, d_{34} and d_{36}. At the phase change at $23·7°$ C d_{14} behaves anomalously, rising from around $3·33 \times 10^{-10}$ coulombs/newton in the middle of the ferroelectric region to $2·33 \times 10^{-9}$ coulombs/newton at $25°$ C; the other constants in the orthorhombic phase are $d_{25} = -5·6 \times 10^{-11}$ and $d_{36} = 1·16 \times 10^{-11}$ at $25°$ C. It should be noted that d_{14} is related to the constant h_{14} via the elastic compliance c_{44}^D which is constant in value over the ferroelectric range, but rises slowly above $24°$ C, and via the permittivity ϵ_{11}. The combined effect of these is that h_{14} remains virtually constant with temperature between $-10°$ C and $+45°$ C. Thus the field produced in the x-direction by shear strain about the x-axis is fairly independent of temperature over a limited range. This fact makes practical the use of an X-cut crystal as a transducer in a microphone or gramophone pick-up.

The ferroelectric behaviour will be further discussed in a later section.

Ammonium Dihydrogen Phosphate (ADP)

This material was developed during World War II in response to the demand for improved ultrasonic transducers for underwater application. Its chemical formula is $NH_4H_2PO_4$ and it crystallizes in the tetragonal class as also does potassium dihydrogen phosphate (KDP), which is a ferroelectric. ADP, having no water of crystallization, does not dehydrate and is stable at temperatures up to $100°$ C. This means that it can handle relatively large acoustic power without breakdown. The piezoelectric constants are d_{14}, d_{24} and d_{36} of which the first two are negligibly small. d_{36} varies from $5 \cdot 16 \times 10^{-11}$ coulombs/newton at $0° C$ to $4 \cdot 32 \times 10^{-11}$ coulombs/newton at $100° C$. This value is smaller than d_{14} in Rochelle Salt which, consequently, would be first choice where large deflexions for a given field were required. The greater chemical and thermal stability of ADP, however, makes it preferable for many applications.

On account of their symmetry, both ADP and KDP have two relative permittivities $\epsilon_{11} = \epsilon_{22}$ and ϵ_{33} and, for the free crystal, ϵ_{11} falls steadily from about 100 at $-120° C$ to 50 at $+100° C$; ϵ_{33} is of the order of 15 at room temperature.

EDT and DKT

These abbreviations are used for ethylene diamine tartrate and dipotassium tartrate respectively. Both belong to the monoclinic class and both have the advantages of little or no water of crystallization, little mechanical loss when vibrating and high electromechanical coupling coefficients. In both cases it is possible to cut slabs for which the piezoelectric constants are independent of temperature. EDT has the chemical formula $C_6H_{14}N_2O_6$ and DKT is $K_2C_4H_4O_6 - \frac{1}{2}H_2O$. The principal d-coefficients are of the same order as those found for ADP, i.e. in the region of 10^{-11} coulombs/newton. Full information on preparation and properties of both crystals have been given by Mason[37] in his book, in which other piezoelectric crystals are also discussed.

Ferroelectricity

Reference has been made to the ten crystal classes exhibiting pyroelectricity. This is the name given to the spontaneous polarization, present in polar crystals, which is a function of temperature. Unlike the case of a ferromagnetic material, where the spontaneous magnetic polarization is revealed by the presence of 'magnetic poles' at the surface of the specimen, the polarization charge at the surface of a dielectric material, arising from its spontaneous polarization, is almost invariably neutralized by the acquisition of free counter-charges either by conduction from within the body of the crystal, or from some external source. However, the dipole moment of a polar material is a function of temperature, so that if the temperature of the specimen is varied, charge will flow to or from the surfaces as the countercharge adjusts itself to the new value of polarization. In this way the spontaneous polarization of the dielectric is revealed; the phenomenon is called the pyroelectric effect.

Ferroelectric materials are a sub-group of the pyroelectrics. In the straight-forward pyroelectric the direction of the spontaneous polarization cannot be reversed by the application of an electric

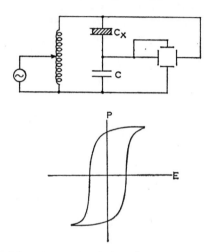

Fig. 36. (a) Circuit for a ferroelectric hysteresis loop tracer, (b) Hysteresis loop for BaTiO₃

field; in the ferroelectric it can. Thus the ferroelectric crystal can be 'switched' by application of a field and a hysteresis is associated with the switching. If a graph of applied field against polarization is drawn a typical hysteresis loop is obtained, similar to the B–H loop for a ferromagnetic.

A ferroelectric hysteresis loop may readily be demonstrated on an oscilloscope by means of the circuit of Fig. 36(a) due to Sawyer and Tower[39] and a typical loop for BaTiO₃ is shown in Fig. 36(b). In the absence of switching the voltages across C and C_X will be inversely proportional to their capacities and, neglecting losses, will be in phase. The oscilloscope exhibits a straight line at a small angle to the horizontal if C has a fairly large capacity. When the ferro-electric crystal, C_X, switches there is a transfer of the surface counter-charge, Q_s, round the circuit such that if, in the initial state, there was a charge $+Q_s$ on the upper face of the crystal there will be $-Q_s$ after switching. The total charge transfer is therefore $2Q_s = 2P_sA$ where P_s is the spontaneous polarization and A the electrode area. The hysteresis effect arises due to there being a threshold value of the field required across the crystal before it switches. When switching occurs the voltage across C will change by $2Q_s/C$, giving a Y-deflexion which is proportional to the spontaneous polarization, P_s, of the crystal, provided that all the ferroelectric domains are switched. Domains are regions in which the polarization is all in a given direction and in most crystals there is a large number of such regions having different orientations. The reversal of the net macroscopic dipole moment of the crystal occurs through nucleation and growth of domains favourably oriented with respect to the applied field.

The existence of a hysteresis loop is proof of the presence of spontaneous polarization in the crystal; the absence of a loop, however, is not proof that there is no spontaneous polarization, but simply that it cannot be reversed by the field applied.

Ferroelectricity is generally exhibited below a specific temperature for any one material, called its Curie temperature. Above this temperature thermal agitation is sufficient to destroy the co-operative ordering of the dipoles which gives rise to the spontaneous polariza-tion. Thus the transition from a paraelectric to a ferroelectric state is essentially a disorder to order charge. The ordering is accompanied by a change of crystal symmetry which may be a change from one crystal class to another, as in Rochelle Salt, or simply a change to lower symmetry within the same class. These are essentially phase changes, and can be classified thermodynamically as first or second order. This is discussed further in a later section.

Ferroelectric Materials

A number of ways have been proposed in which ferroelectric materials can be grouped phenomenologically. Merz[40] divides them into 'hard' and 'soft' materials by whether they are water-soluble or not.

Känzig[41] classifies them into those which polarize along only one axis ('up' or 'down') and those which can polarize along several axes that are equivalent in the non-polar state. The latter is considered a more fundamental classification and will be used here.

Uniaxial ferroelectrics

Rochelle Salt and related tartrates.

Potassium dihydrogen phosphate and related materials XH_2YO_4, with X = K, Rb or Cs and Y = P or As.

$(NH_4)_2SO_4$ and $(NH_4)_2BeF_4$.

Colemanite, $CaB_3O_4(OH)_3 . H_2O$.

Thiourea, $(NH_2)_2CS$.

T.G.S. (triglycine sulphate) $(CH_2NH_2COOH)_3H_2SO_4$ and the related salts such as triglycine fluoberyllate (TGF).

Guanidine aluminium sulphate hexahydrate (GASH) $(CN_3H_6)Al(SO_4)_26H_2O$.

Lithium selenite $LiH_3(SeO_3)_2$ and related salts.

It should be noted that GASH falls in the first class by default since, as it has no known Curie point, it is impossible to make any statement based on its non-polar state.

Multiaxial ferroelectrics

Barium titanate ($BaTiO_3$) and related materials with perovskite crystal structure.

Certain niobates of the type of lead metaniobate ($Pb(NbO_3)_2$ with a pyrochlore type of crystal structure.

Certain alums of the type $XY(SO_4)_212H_2O$ where X is an ammonium ion and Y a specially symmetrical ion like Al or Cr.

Ammonium cadmium sulphate $(NH_4)_2Cd_2(SO_4)_3$.

The above is not a complete list of known ferroelectrics, since new ones are being discovered continuously. A comprehensive list up to 1962 has been given by Merz[40].

Antiferroelectricity and ferrielectricity

Continuing the analogy with magnetic materials, the phenomenon of antiferroelectricity was recognized by Kittel[42]. He suggested that,

10

in some materials, spontaneous polarization may exist with the dipoles in antiparallel arrangements, such that the net polarization was zero. Lead zirconate ($PbZrO_3$) was proposed as an example by Shirane et al.[43] who showed that it is ferroelectric in high fields, but not in low. This could be explained on the basis of the high field unbalancing the antiparallel polarizations so that a new polarization was produced. Shirane also showed, by X-ray analysis, that there is an antiparallel array of ionic displacements at room temperature. This crystal phase could be described in terms of equivalent sublattices with equal, but opposite, polarizations. In line with the practice in magnetics the induced polarization at high fields can be described as ferrielectricity.

Antiferroelectric transitions have been reported in $PbHfO_3$, $NaNbO_3$ (which is ferrielectric), WO_3 (also exhibits ferroelectric phase) $NH_4H_2PO_4$ and isomorphous ammonium salts, $(NH_4)_2H_3IO_6$, AgH_3IO_6, and certain alums.

Ferroelectric Domains

A spontaneously polarized, ferroelectric crystal will usually minimize its electrostatic energy by forming domains. These are regions, of area large compared with a molecule, in which the dipoles are all aligned parallel to each other. In a uniaxial crystal the domains will be 180° ones, i.e. the polarization will be in opposite directions in adjacent domains. In the multiaxial crystals, adjacent domains may be polarized in directions having an angle between them equal to that between corresponding crystallographic directions in the non-polar phase.

Domains can be rendered visible by suitable techniques. In the case of multiaxial crystals, such as barium titanate, the cubic symmetry leads to domains polarized 90° apart. If illuminated by polarized light, and viewed through an analyser, the domains are seen by virtue of the differing rotation of the plane of polarization of the light caused by the different domains. Unfortunately, so far as this effect is concerned, the effect on the light of antiparallel polarizations is precisely the same, so that the domains do not become visible.

For the uniaxial crystals Pearson and Feldmann[44] have produced a modification of the Bitter techniques well-known in magnetism. A colloidal solution of yellow sulphur in hexane is found to deposit preferentially on negative dipole ends, whilst colloidal red lead oxide (Pb_3O_4) deposits preferentially on positive dipole ends. Using these solutions domain structures have been shown up in great detail.

Domain studies have shown that, whilst there is strong coupling between antiparallel domains, the coupling between 90° domains is weak. Energetically there is also very little difference between an antiparallel and a parallel array of dipoles. The combination of these facts leads to the conclusion that switching in a ferroelectric will occur mainly by nucleation and growth of domains along the ferroelectric axis, assuming the applied field to be along this axis. There is little evidence of a wall motion, similar to that encountered in ferromagnetics, whereby a domain favourably oriented with respect to the field increases its area by motion of the boundary between it and an unfavourably oriented domain.

It is generally possible to 'pole' a ferroelectric crystal so that its polarization is all in one direction. This is done by taking it through the Curie point, from the paraelectric to the ferroelectric phase, whilst applying a large electric field across it, in the appropriate direction.

Molecular Mechanisms

A large number of possible mechanisms of ferroelectricity has been discussed and, to date, no completely satisfactory quantitative theory has been forthcoming. It is clear from careful X-ray analysis, however, that the dipole moment is associated with distortion of molecular groups, whilst the co-operative alignment of these dipoles, to give spontaneous polarization, is a function of the interatomic bonding in the crystal.

In the case of the uniaxial crystals, and of sulphates in the multiaxial group, the dipole moment is due to the deformation of atomic groups such as SO_4, SeO_4, AsO_4, etc., in which the undeformed state is a symmetrical arrangement of the oxygen ions around the central sulphur (or other) ion. At the Curie temperature the crystal strains spontaneously, the central ion is slightly displaced and the atomic groups acquire a dipole moment. The spontaneous strain is due to ordering of the hydrogen bonds (present in all the uniaxial ferro-electrics), corresponding to the order-disorder phase change in the crystal. The ordered bonds act to align the induced dipoles causing spontaneous polarization. The determining factor in the order-disorder phase change is the (thermodynamic) free energy associated with the crystal structure, and is outside the scope of the present text. It has been dealt with by Forsbergh[45].

The case of the multiaxial ferroelectrics of perovskite and pyro-chlore structure differs somewhat. Here the basic molecular structure is an octahedral arrangement of oxygen ions around a central ion such as Ti in $BaTiO_3$. Below the Curie point the Ti ion is shifted from its symmetrical position, giving a dipole moment to the molecular group. The alignment of the moments, however, is not due to hydrogen bonds, but to coupling between the oxygen ions. These are partially ionic and partially covalent, and the directional property of the covalent bond is responsible for the alignment. The effect can be thought of in terms of a Mosotti-type internal field. Starting with the Ti ion at the centre of the oxygen octahedron the net dipole moment is zero. Thermal agitation displaces the Ti ion against its oxygen surroundings which causes a small shift of the oxygen ions. This shift causes an increase in the effective field at the Ti ion in the direction of the original displacement so that the displacement is increased. At a critical temperature this feedback effect is sufficient to overcome the thermal motion and causes a permanent displacement of the Ti ion. Since, in any oxygen octahedron in the perovskite structure, two of the oxygen ions are shared with adjacent octahedra there is a coupling from one to the other, which will lead to displacement of all the Ti ions in the same direction.

Dielectric Behaviour

The total permittivity of normal dielectrics decreases with decreasing temperature. In ferroelectric materials the permittivity and suscepti-bility increase with decreasing temperature, going through a sharp maximum at the Curie temperature and thereafter falling further, as temperature decreases. Above the Curie temperature the dielectric susceptibility follows a Curie-Weiss law, as predicted by the 'Mosotti catastrophe' discussed in Chapter 5, i.e.

$$\chi \doteq \frac{C}{T - T_c} \qquad (9.12)$$

where C is the Curie constant. For ferroelectrics containing hydrogen bonding, C is the order of $100°\,K$ whilst for the oxygen octahedra type it is in the region of $10^{4°}\,K$. The temperature dependence of

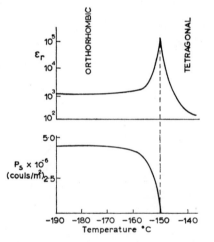

Fig. 37(a). Permittivity and polarization of KDP

permittivity and of spontaneous polarization for KDP is shown in Fig. 37(a) and for Rochelle Salt in Fig. 37(b) over the region of their Curie temperatures.

The high permittivity, typically of the order of 10,000, at the Curie temperature, is readily understandable. At this temperature the ions are on the point of moving into or out of the position corresponding to spontaneous polarization; consequently an applied field will be able to produce relatively large shifts, with big changes in dipole

moment, corresponding to a high permittivity. The falling susceptibility below T_c corresponds to an increasing degree of spontaneous
saturation of polarization in the material.

The permittivity is strongly anisotropic in the ferroelectric phase of
all crystals, particularly in the uniaxial ones. In a direction perpendicular to the ferroelectric axis in a uniaxial crystal, the permittivity is much lower than along the axis, but exhibits little or no

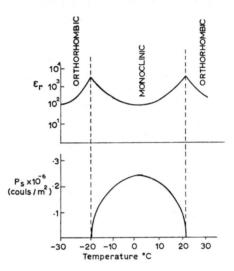

Fig. 37(b). RS as a function of temperature

anomalous temperature dependence. In KDP, for instance, the
relative permittivity along the axis is 1100 and perpendicular to it is
12 at $100°\,K$; in Rochelle Salt the parallel value is 1000 and the
perpendicular 10 at room temperature.

Polyaxial ferroelectrics that are cubic and dielectrically isotropic
in the non-polar phase become strongly anisotropic in the polar
phase. The permittivity along the axis of polarization is *lower* than
that at right angles to it. In $BaTiO_3$ the relative permittivity along
the c-axis (principal ferroelectric axis) is ~ 160, and perpendicular

to it is 5000 at room temperature. It should be noted that the measurements have to be made on a single-domain crystal.

The high relative permittivities of ferroelectric materials is potentially of considerable practical importance, and much effort has been put into taking advantage of them in capacitors. Piezoelectric behaviour and chemical instability have, however, generally caused considerable difficulty in practical applications.

The a.c. permittivity for a ferroelectric crystal will vary with the frequency used in the measurement and with the size of the crystal. At low frequencies the piezoelectric deformations can follow the periodic change of applied field, so that the crystal is mechanically unconstrained and the free permittivity is measured. At high frequencies, higher than the mechanical resonance frequency of the specimen, the strain is unable to follow the applied field. The permittivity measured is then that of a 'clamped' crystal. In non-piezoelectric crystals these two permittivities are, of course, identical, but in ferroelectrics they can differ by as much as several orders of magnitude, the 'free' value being invariably greater than the 'clamped'. For $BaTiO_3$ the relative permittivity ϵ_{11} has a free value of 4000 and a clamped value of 500 at room temperature.

Dielectric relaxation frequencies in all ferroelectrics appear, from experimental results, to be in the microwave to far infra-red regions, depending on material and temperature. Despite this, very large values of ϵ'', i.e. high losses, have been reported for various ferroelectric materials in the microwave range. It seems fairly certain that these losses are connected with domain wall oscillations; in a $BaTiO_3$ crystal, properly poled so that it is a single domain, the microwave loss is much reduced.

Thermodynamic Considerations

Macroscopic phenomenological theories based on thermodynamics have been propounded, relatively successfully, by a number of workers. These are reviewed by Forsbergh[45] but the details of the calculations are beyond the scope of this book. However, one may adopt a fairly simple viewpoint of the significance of thermodynamic relations by considering the statistical interpretation of entropy as a measure of order. A well-ordered system is one having a low entropy whilst increasing disorder increases entropy. Treating only the dipoles in the ferroelectric material, they are clearly ordered in the ferro-electric phase and become disordered as the temperature passes through the Curie point to the paraelectric phase. Thus the transition should be accompanied by an increase in entropy. Thermo-dynamically this usually corresponds to a first-order transition for which ΔS, the change in entropy, is finite. On the other hand, order can be interpreted in terms of the regularity of the crystal lattice, and we have seen that the ferroelectric state is usually one of lower symmetry than the paraelectric state. Thus the change from ferroelectric to paraelectric will correspond to increasing crystallographic order and entropy should decrease. If this cancels out the increase due to dipole order, so that $S = 0$, the transition is usually thermodynamically of second order. In ferroelectrics the entropies of transition vary from $2 \times 10^{-3} R$ for Rochelle Salt to $0.8R$ for lead titanate, where R is the gas constant. From this it may be concluded that the lead titanate transition is thermodynamically of first order, whilst in Rochelle Salt the transition is of second order and involves a crystallographic change as well of ordering of the dipoles. Barium titanate, in which the ferroelectric behaviour is due to displacement of the Ti ions and does not involve a crystallographic change, may be expected to show principally order-disorder characteristics, and this is suggested by its transition entropy being an order of magnitude greater than that of Rochelle Salt. Table IV shows the Curie temperatures and transition entropies for a number of materials.

Table IV

CRYSTAL	Curie temperature °K	ΔS
$PbTiO_3$	760	$0.8R$
KH_2PO_4	122	$0.37R$
$KNbO_3$	700	$0.14R$
$BaTiO_3$	393	$0.06R$
$Cd_2Nb_2O_7$	188	$0.04R$
Rochelle Salt	296	$0.002R$

CHAPTER 10
Dielectric Devices

Introduction
In this chapter applications of the special dielectric properties already discussed are considered. The term 'device' is used here in the sense of an article fabricated to fulfil a particular function by making use of special physical properties specific to the material. Such a definition would include any application of dielectrics, such as to ordinary electrical insulators; but it is not intended to discuss routine items here, attention is focused on applications of such properties as piezoelectricity and ferroelectricity and to cases where new fabrication techniques have led to improved performances in well established applications.

The Crystal Resonator
The earliest application of the piezoelectric effect was in the use of quartz crystals as electromechanical resonators. It was pointed out in Chapter 9 that mechanical resonance could occur in a quartz crystal, excited by the application of an alternating field, by virtue of the converse piezoelectric effect. The equivalent electrical circuit of the oscillating crystal is that of a series-parallel resonant circuit, shown in Fig. 35. The circuit is characterized by a very high equivalent electrical Q factor, of the order of several thousand, which is to be compared with maximum values in the region of 100–200 attainable in normal LC circuits at comparable frequencies. The applications include frequency control of oscillators and selective filters. Provided that the ambient temperature does not vary, the frequency at which a crystal resonates will be extremely stable, since it depends only on its mechanical dimensions. In filter applications, the high Q factor permits the design of a filter capable of attenuating or passing an extremely narrow band of frequencies, giving it a very high selectivity.

For both applications it is important that the piezoelectric behaviour should not vary with temperature. In quartz, the piezoelectric

143

coefficients are temperature-dependent, but the dependence changes in magnitude and sign with crystallographic direction. Thus it is possible to cut a slab with zero temperature coefficient. This cut, called a GT-cut, is illustrated in Fig. 38, and is used in frequency-stabilizing applications. Where maximum activity is the primary

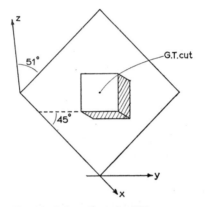

Fig. 38. Orientation of a GT-cut, zero temperature-coefficient quartz crystal

consideration, an X-cut crystal is used, this having the greatest value of electromechanical coupling coefficient, defined by

$$\kappa^2 = \frac{h^2 \epsilon^s}{c^D} \tag{10.1}$$

where the symbols have the significance given in the previous chapter. k^2 of the total input electrical energy is converted into stored mechanical energy. The X-cut crystal has a poor temperature stability but is useful as a generator of high-frequency ultrasonic waves. A full discussion of quartz and other crystals in the above types of application has been given by Mason[37].

Piezoelectric Ceramics

The use of single crystals in piezoelectric applications is necessarily limited by the size and shape of available crystals. Of recent years a number of ceramic materials has been developed in which barium titanate powder is compressed into the desired shape and sintered at high temperature. For different applications various additives are used, which may be:

(a) *Mineralizers and fluxes.* These are materials which affect the structure of the ceramic without altering the dielectric properties. They are generally used in small quantities ($\sim 1\%$) to alter the rate of reaction and crystal growth during firing.

(b) *Diluents.* Additives which do not dissolve in the ferroelectric material (usually barium titanate) form a separate phase of low permittivity, thereby reducing the permittivity of the ceramic without altering its Curie temperatures.

(c) *Soluble oxides.* Oxides which dissolve in, and form a solid solution with the barium titanate will alter the Curie temperatures and ferroelectric behaviour.

The fabrication technique permits the formation of any shape and size of specimen by use of suitable moulds. The ceramic, after firing, can be given a permanent polarization in a required direction by a suitable poling procedure, which consists of immersing the ceramic element in oil above the Curie temperature ($\sim 120° \text{C}$) and allowing it to cool with an electric field applied across it in the desired direction. Relatively low fields, of the order of 4×10^4 V/m, are adequate to produce almost complete orientation of the induced polarization for single-phase oxide ceramics. When a diluent is used, a porcelain-type structure results and fields between 1 and 2×10^6 V/m, applied for $\frac{1}{2}$ h to 6 h are required for complete poling. The addition of small amounts of calcium and lead titanate yields good temperature stability and higher piezoelectric activity. A typical such mixed titanate material has the following constants:

$$d_{31} = 0{\cdot}73 \times 10^{-10} \text{ coulombs/newton}$$
$$d_{33} = 1{\cdot}605 \times 10^{-10} \text{ coulombs/newton}$$
$$\epsilon_{33}^{T} = 1630$$

from which it will be seen that the piezoelectric activity is about two orders of magnitude greater, and that the relative permittivity is nearly 400 times greater, than the values for quartz. Even higher values have been obtained with lead zirconate-barium titanate mixed ceramics.

In addition, electrical and mechanical Q factors of several hundred are obtained, the materials are mechanically strong and they can withstand large electric stresses (~ 50 to 100 kV/in.).

The major disadvantage of all these materials is the relatively large temperature-dependence of their properties, particularly of the piezoelectric coefficients and relative permittivity. A limitation on the materials also arises, in alternating current applications, from a rapid increase in dielectric loss, with consequent lowering of Q factor, at high electric stresses. The losses become prohibitively high in the region upwards of 500 V r.m.s. per inch. The increased loss leads to rapid rise of temperature during operation with consequent deterioration of performance and eventually loss of polarization. The development of the ceramic piezoelectric has greatly extended the number of applications of the effect, and some of these will now be described.

Piezoelectric Transformers

A piezoelectric ceramic bar may have four electrodes fired on to it either in a ring-type arrangement, shown in Fig. 39(*a*) or transversely

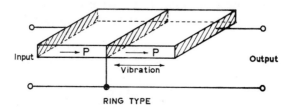

Fig. 39(*a*). Piezoelectric transformers; ring type

as shown in Fig. 39(*b*). A periodic exciting field is applied between the left-hand pair of electrodes causing mechanical oscillation of the bar. If its length is an integral number of half-wavelengths for mechanical stress waves, the bar will act as a resonant device and a standing wave distribution of large amplitude elastic strain and stress will result. The right-hand pair of electrodes will have a voltage set up between them, by direct piezoelectric effect, which is an amplified version of the exciting voltage.

The ceramic transformer is best suited as a high-voltage transformer, operating at low current levels, since its input and output impedances are high compared with conventional transformers.

The most useful type for transformer applications is the transverse one, as its voltage gain can be controlled by variation of the dimensions of the bar. In the ring type the voltage amplification is a function

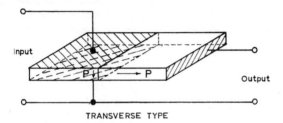

TRANSVERSE TYPE

Fig. 39(*b*). Piezoelectric transformers; transverse type

only of mechanical Q and electromechanical coupling coefficient, and is independent of the bar geometry.

In a typical application, using mixed titanate ceramic, a maximum voltage amplification of 30 is obtained at 14 kc/s, with an efficiency of about 50%.

Full details of design procedure have been given by Rosen[46].

Ceramic Filters

Single piezoelectric crystals have long been used as elements in electric filters, their very high Q factors and stable resonance frequency making them preferable to LC circuits in very selective filters. A very full discussion of crystal filters has been given by Mason[47]. The single crystal filter is generally limited to frequencies in the region of 100 kc/s upwards because, for lower frequencies, a very large crystal is required, which is difficult and expensive to obtain. A piezoelectric ceramic is not subject to this limitation so that low-frequency ceramic filters can be made relatively cheaply.

The simplest type of filter is obtained by driving a long, thin bar in longitudinal resonance in precisely the configuration used for the piezoelectric transformer. For frequencies below about 10 kc/s the length of bar required becomes inconveniently large.

This limitation is overcome by use of the 'bimorph' construction illustrated in Fig. 40(a). A ceramic element, varying in length on application of a field, is firmly bonded to a second element of equal flexural compliance. The effect of an increase in length of the first element is to cause a bending of the combination, motion occurring at right angles to the length. The actual lateral displacement may be many times the length increase and, by direct piezoelectric effect, it causes a voltage to appear between the electrodes of the second

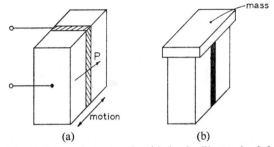

Fig. 40. Bimorph construction (a) simple, (b) mass-loaded

element. The centre conductor serves both as a common electrode for the two elements and also as an electrostatic screen between them. It may also provide the bonding and an increased mechanical strength.

The mechanical resonance is given by Rayleigh's expression for a vibrating reed, which is

$$f = \frac{m^2 t}{2\pi \sqrt{(12)} L^2} \cdot \left(\frac{Y}{\rho}\right)^{1/2} \tag{10.2}$$

where $Y =$ Young's modulus, $\rho =$ density, $t =$ thickness, and $L =$ length, m is a number, whose value depends on the mode of vibration and, for the fundamental, is 1·875. Frequency may be lowered by reduction of thickness and increase of length, but below 100 c/s the element becomes inconveniently long and thin. In such a case the element is mass-loaded, as shown in Fig. 40(b), the lower practical limit to frequency being in the region of 20 c/s. The frequency of the mass-loaded element is given approximately by

$$f = \frac{1}{2\pi} \cdot \left(\frac{1}{KM}\right)^{1/2} \tag{10.3}$$

where M is the mass and K is the compliance, given by

$$K = \frac{4L^3}{wt^3}$$

where w = width, and t, L are the thickness and length of the rectangular mass.

Disc-shaped ceramic elements have been used by Campbell and MacSwan[48] in ladder filters which, because of size limitations on the discs, were restricted to the frequency range 50–500 kc/s. The filter characteristics depended upon the electromechanical coupling and mechanical Q factors of the discs, and it was found possible to design filters having pass-bands from 2% to 20% of the centre frequency, with a pole of attenuation on both sides of the pass-band. By using a ceramic disc, oscillating in the radial mode, they produced an interstage I.F. transformer suitable for use in a transistor amplifier. The disc is made a three-terminal device with a common, continuous electrode on one face and a dot and annulus on the other. Input was between dot and common electrode and output between annulus and common electrode. The input to output impedance ratio is a function of the electrode areas, and the magnitude of the impedance for a given frequency is a function of the disc thickness. Typical values, for a transistor circuit, were 5 kΩ input and 1 kΩ output.

Piezoelectric Transducers

The name transducer, in this connexion, is generally applied to a device in which electrical energy is converted to mechanical or vice-versa. Dealing first with the former case, the piezoelectric transducer is widely applied to the generation of ultrasonic waves. Any piezoelectric crystal may be used to generate ultrasonic vibrations but, where high power is required, only quartz and titanate ceramics are suitable.

The quartz crystal transducer usually employs an X-cut crystal, vibrating in the longitudinal mode. If λ is the wavelength of the standing wave excited in the crystal, resonance occurs when its length $l = n\lambda/2$ when n is an integer. The velocity of sound in the crystal is determined by its density ρ and Young's modulus Y by the usual relation

$$v = \left(\frac{Y}{\rho}\right)^{1/2}.$$

Thus, using $f = v\lambda$, the frequency of the wave generated is given by

$$f = \frac{n}{2l}\left(\frac{Y}{\rho}\right)^{1/2}. \tag{10.4}$$

For $n = 1$, using the known constants for quartz, $f = 2700l$ kc/s where l is in millimetres. In practice this is a little low, and the empirical value $f = 2830l$ kc/s is generally used.

The crystal is usually mounted so that it can be immersed in liquid, which represents the acoustic load. The equivalent circuit of the loaded crystal is given in Fig. 41. It will be seen that, in addition to the elements present in the equivalent circuit of the free crystal (Fig. 35), there is an additional shunt resistance R_S, accounting for dielectric losses, and a series resistance R_L which represents the effect of the acoustic load. R_L is, in fact, the 'motional impedance' of the loaded crystal and this has been calculated by Hartmann and Trolle[49] for a simple circular plate. For an X-cut quartz crystal, radiating into water on one side and air on the other, this leads to

$$R_L = 12 \cdot 5 \left(\frac{l^2}{S}\right) \quad M\Omega \tag{10.5}$$

where S is the radiating area of the plate. Since l is always directly proportional to the wavelength, it emerges that R_L is inversely proportional to the square of frequency, and since it is represented as a series loss resistance it is clear that, for a given voltage applied across the equivalent circuit (i.e. a constant excitation), the power lost in R_L increases with frequency. In other words, the power transferred to the acoustic load increases with increasing frequency. This will more than offset the reduction in the maximum permissible voltage across the crystal due to decreasing thickness. For an X-cut quartz crystal of 2 in. diameter operating at 1 Mc/s, $R_L = 50$ kΩ.

Usually vibration does not occur uniformly over the crystal area, and for high-power applications the power generated has to be limited to a value such that no part of the crystal exceeds its elastic limit. As the frequency is increased, with consequent reduction of crystal thickness, the danger of mechanical fracture and electrical breakdown increases. The useful upper limit for quartz, operating in the fundamental mode ($n = 1$), is about 2 Mc/s, although up to 200 Mc/s can be obtained at low power by the use of harmonics.

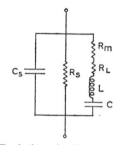

Fig. 41. Equivalent circuit of a liquid-loaded
piezoelectric transducer

The radiation from a circular plate source is in the form of a highly directional beam if the ratio of plate diameter to wavelength is large. There is then little loss in the acoustic medium due to dispersion. However, any discontinuity in the medium, such as the walls of the containing vessel, will set up reflections causing standing waves which inhibit power transfer to the medium. For a plane glass-walled vessel containing oil the reflection coefficient is 70%, and gives rise to complex standing-wave patterns in the medium. To set up a continuous wave it is necessary to absorb sound reaching the walls of the vessel.

To a first approximation the acoustic power delivered by the transducer is given by V^2/R_L watts, where V is the applied voltage. For the case, quoted above, of $R_L = 50$ kΩ it is clear that, for ultrasonic

11

power of the order of 100 W, we require something like 2 kV across the crystal. Thus insulation in the transducer must be fairly heavy and the design of a practical transducer is a complex problem. Commercial devices are marketed by a number of companies for a wide range of applications.

The mechanical strength and high breakdown voltage of titanate ceramics makes them very suitable as electromechanical transducer elements. The material can be pre-formed to any desired shape for a particular application. For example, a bowl-shaped element, pre-polarized in the direction of its thickness, will oscillate in the thickness-mode and the ultrasonic wave generated by it will be focused to a point. This is an extremely useful feature.

Mixed titanate elements are usually used, with a proportion of lead titanate added to raise the Curie point, so that if the element heats when operating, it will not become depolarized. To minimize heating of the ceramic element the material should have a low dielectric loss. Cobalt oxide, which acts as a mineralizer, is a suitable additive, giving a glassy ceramic with very small crystallites, which has relatively low loss.

The actual mechanism by which the ferroelectric ceramic acts as a piezoelectric material can be described in terms of the molecular behaviour. The previous chapter has described how ferroelectricity is induced in $BaTiO_3$ by displacement of the titanate group of atoms. Accompanying this displacement there is a considerable change in length of the crystal in the c-axis direction, this being an increase for one direction of displacement and a decrease for the opposite direction. When a polarizing field is applied to the fresh crystal, domains having polarization opposite to the field direction switch, when the field is big enough, by displacement of the titanate ions, and the length of the crystal changes in the direction of the applied field by as much as 1 part in 3000 for a field of 10 kV/cm. In the newly-prepared polycrystalline ceramic the individual crystallites will be polarized in random directions so that the material will exhibit electrostriction on the application of a d.c. field, i.e. reversal of the field will not reverse the change in dimensions of the sample. This is because crystallites polarized nearly parallel to the field will line up with it, with corresponding change in length, whilst the remainder will be relatively unaffected, whatever the direction of applied field. It is estimated that the percentage of domains lining up is between 7 and 10% of the whole. The value of the total increase in length in the field direction is between 5 and 7 parts in 10^4, for a field of 30 kV/cm.

If an a.c. field is superimposed on the d.c. field, changes in length proportional to the a.c. are induced, i.e. they reverse sign with reversal of the a.c. field. This is the piezoelectric effect which induces mechanical vibration in the crystal. The d.c. polarizing field is generally replaced by the poling procedure described above. The induced remanent polarization acts in the same way as the applied d.c. field. Prepolarized mixed titanate ceramic can be produced with an electromechanical coupling coefficient as high as 60%, making it the most efficient of the piezoelectric transducer materials. Also its motional impedance is a factor of 100 lower than that of quartz; for a given output power, therefore, the voltage required across the ceramic is 1/100 of that required by a quartz crystal. However, the ceramic has a much higher mechanical loss resistance and the mechanical Q factors are much lower than with quartz. Because of its high permittivity the ceramic element has a high static capacity, typically of the order of 0·05 μF. The effective impedance of the element is therefore in the region of 2 Ω at 1 Mc/s, with a loaded Q factor of about 30. Typical power outputs are of the order of 1 W/cm^2 which, with a prefocused bowl-shaped specimen, gives about 3 kW/cm^2 at the focal point.

A full discussion of ultrasonic transducers and their applications will be found in Crawford's book[50].

Devices for converting mechanical movement into electricity are mainly applied to the detection of small vibrations. The most obvious examples of these are the gramophone pick-up and the microphone. Dielectric loss is not an important factor in these applications, the principal requirements being high piezoelectric coefficients and good thermal stability. For many years the material best meeting these requirements was Rochelle Salt, but the new synthetic crystals, particularly ADP and KDP, have similar piezoelectric properties and do not suffer the disadvantage of being hygroscopic. Their somewhat lower sensitivity, compared with Rochelle Salt, can be compensated for by the 'bimorph' type of construction, described in connexion with filter elements. Ceramic piezoelectrics have also been developed for this type of application, having zirconium dioxide as an additive, which produces a high piezoelectric coefficient by virtue of raising the lower transition point of $BaTiO_3$ to room temperature. The elements are made as bimorphs, consisting of two thin plates of ceramic soldered on to opposite sides of a thin copper sheet. The pieces are polarized transversely in opposite directions and movement of the stylus puts one piece under compression and the other under tension about the neutral plane of the copper. The output is about 1 v peak for a normal recording.

Capacitors

The very high permittivities of ferroelectric materials offer the possibility of capacitors having large capacitance combined with small size. Much development work was put into producing barium titanate based capacitors, which led to the development of ceramics suitable for this application. Barium titanate ceramic itself is not very satisfactory, since its permittivity is fairly temperature-sensitive and relatively low (below 2000). More important, however, it is a material very prone to loss with a power factor of more than 10%. The losses can be reduced by certain additives which operate by altering the ceramic structure and reducing the dielectric conductivity. But this usually also results in a lowering of the Curie temperature so that, when operating in the region of 20° C, the temperature-dependence of permittivity is increased. Zirconium and stannic oxides, which dissolve in $BaTiO_3$, reduce the losses without worsening the temperature stability, but also have the effect of reducing permittivity. The best compromise is probably the addition of nickel or ferric oxides. These reduce the power factor to the region of 5%, and can give maximum permittivities in the region of 4000 with a temperature variation of permittivity of around 0·5% per °C in the region of room temperature for NiO additive, or a permittivity of 2000 with a temperature stability of 0·1% per °C for FeO additive.

The substitution of strontium for barium lowers the transition temperatures so that the upper Curie temperature can be brought below 20° C. The very high permittivity (~ 5000) just above the Curie point is then obtained, but this falls to ~3000 at 100° C. If a small amount of MgO is added the losses can be brought down to 0·2%. Small-size capacitors for domestic radio applications have been manufactured with this material. For any application where precision and constancy of capacitance is important, titanate based capacitors cannot be used.

Thin-Film Capacitors

Since the capacitance of a parallel-plate condenser is inversely proportional to the distance between the plates, reducing this distance to very small values should provide high-value capacitors of very small size. Since, however, the maximum realizable dielectric strength of many dielectrics is of the order of 10^6 V/cm, a condenser with plates 1000 Å (10^{-5} cm) apart would break down with 10 V across it. This is much too low for most valve circuit applications, but the advent of the transistor, with its low working voltages, makes the use of thin-film capacitors a practical proposition.

The capacitance of a parallel-plate condenser is given by

$$C = \frac{\epsilon A}{d} \text{ farads.} \tag{10.6}$$

For 1 cm^2 plates separated by 1 μ (i.e. 10^{-4} cm) with a dielectric of relative permittivity of 10, such a capacitor would have a capacitance of about 0·8 μF.

The fabrication of thin-film capacitors is usually done by vacuum deposition. A cleaned glass substrate is mounted in a vacuum chamber, with a pressure in the region of 10^{-5} mm Hg, and a film of aluminium is evaporated on to it as the base electrode. The evaporation is normally done by melting the metal on a hot filament, or in an electrically heated crucible, the metal evaporating on to the glass through a mask defining the area to be covered. This is followed by evaporation of the dielectric, typically silicon monoxide, and then by a second aluminium evaporation, providing the second electrode. Suitable masks and shutters ensure the correct geometry for each evaporated layer. After preparation the device exhibits a much lower breakdown voltage than that corresponding to intrinsic breakdown, but it is increased by a 'preforming' treatment in which short pulses of voltage are applied. These appear to have the property of 'burning out' defects which represent high-conductivity paths between the electrodes. The burn-out properties depend on the metal used for the electrodes, aluminium giving the best results.

It is found that the full relative permittivity of the dielectric is rarely reached with most thin films. Silicon monoxide films show a permittivity of 4·5 to 5·5 with a loss factor between 1 % and 3 % up to 1 Mc/s, and a breakdown voltage in excess of 10^6 V/cm. Dielectrics used successfully have been lithium fluoride, ($\epsilon_r \sim 9·5$), zinc sulphide ($\epsilon_r = 7·5$–$8·5$), and magnesium fluoride ($\epsilon_r = 5$), their choice being dictated by ease of evaporation and ability to form good, continuous films. More recent work, with high permittivity materials such as lead titanate and titanium dioxide, has been successful, and capacitors of up to 1 μF per cm^2 with working voltages in the region of 30 V have been produced experimentally.

A further advantage of the thin-film capacitor is that it can readily be built into an evaporation programme in which resistors, connecting wires, and even transistors are produced by successive vacuum depositions. These 'integrated circuits' are at present being actively developed, and are of considerable potential importance.

Dielectric Amplifiers

A ferroelectric has been described earlier as having a hysteresis loop, which defines the relation between dielectric flux density, D, and applied field, E, a typical one for $BaTiO_3$ being shown in Fig. 36(b).

An analogue to the magnetic amplifier can be constructed using a condenser whose dielectric layer is a ferroelectric such as a barium titanate.

If the titanate capacitor has a small a.c. signal applied to it, its capacitance, as far as the a.c. is concerned, is determined by the incremental permittivity which, in turn, is determined by the point on the hysteresis loop at which the capacitor is being operated. Thus, by applying a d.c. bias to vary the operating point, the incremental permittivity can be varied over a wide range. Ceramic dielectrics have been developed which show a large change of incremental permittivity with applied field, stannic oxide being the most effective additive for this purpose. A typical capacity versus bias voltage curve is shown in Fig. 42. One possible application of the device is as a variable capacitor whose value is changed by variation of a d.c. bias voltage.

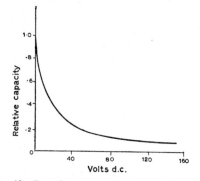

Fig. 42. Capacitance as a function of bias for a mixed-ceramic capacitor

Another possible application is to the construction of a dielectric amplifier analogous to the magnetic amplifier now widely used. Consider the circuit of Fig. 43, in which the ferroelectric condenser is effectively in series with the power supply and the load. If the bias

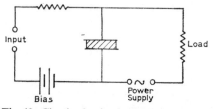

Fig. 43. Circuit of a simple dielectric amplifier

voltage is chosen to give an operating point on the steep part of the capacitance/voltage curve of Fig. 42, the input signal will cause relatively large changes in the capacitance value. So far as the load is concerned the current delivered to it from the power supply is determined by the value of series capacitance. Thus the current in the load is modulated by the input signal. By proper choice of impedances a reasonable power gain may be achieved. Efficiency can be improved by use of a bridge-type circuit shown in Fig. 44.

High gains can be achieved by use of a resonant circuit. The principle of operation is that the ferroelectric condenser, with zero input voltage, has a capacitance in excess of that required for reson-

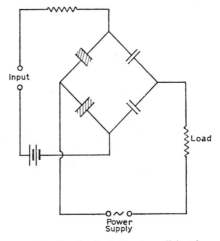

Fig. 44. Circuit of a bridge-type dielectric
amplifier

ance with a suitably-chosen coil at the power supply frequency. The input voltage causes a reduction in capacitance, bringing the circuit nearer to resonance. A multistage resonance-type circuit has been described by Silverstein[51] which employed capacitors made up of 2·5 ml thick ceramic discs. These provided a capacitance change of $\frac{1}{2}\%$ per volt, and an overall voltage gain of 10,000 was achieved with a signal of 100 c/s to 10 kc/s.

Dielectric amplifiers have not been exploited due to the disadvantages of ferroelectric materials, compared with ferromagnetic material performance in magnetic amplifiers. The principal difficulties arise from the temperature-sensitivity of permittivity and the large hysteresis and conduction losses. If these difficulties are over-come, however, the smaller size and weight of dielectric amplifiers offer considerable advantages over comparable magnetic ones.

Space-charge Limited Dielectric Devices

It has been seen in an earlier chapter that the electronic band structure of an insulator can be described by a full valence band, separated from an empty conduction band by a large energy gap of several electron volts. At room temperature there will be relatively few electrons in the conduction band, and these will generally have come from impurity centres with energy levels just below the lower edge of the valence band.

If, however, electrons can be injected into the conduction band they will be free to travel through the crystal, and will give rise to a current if a field is applied. This situation is analogous to that of the vacuum diode, in which the electrons are injected from the cathode into the vacuum and are collected at the anode by application of an electric field. In the dielectric device one electrode will be required to act as an emitter, whilst the other will be required to make a 'blocking' contact with the dielectric, i.e. it must be able to extract the extra electrons from the crystal and not inject any of its own. As in the vacuum diode the flow of current through the device will be space-charge limited, since the injected electrons will form a charge cloud in the crystal. The advantage of this type of current flow is the smoothing-out effect it has on random fluctuations in electron densities and velocities, with consequent reduction of noise. This picture ignores the effects of impurities and flaws in the crystal, which can act as electron traps. If trapping is significant it will severely limit conduction through the crystal. Thus a pure, flaw-free dielectric crystal is likely to be required in this type of application. In practice the best crystals contain an appreciable density of traps, but it is possible to put compensating impurities in the crystal which have the effect of cancelling out the electron traps. Rose[52] and Lampert[53] have calculated that a carefully-grown crystal, which typically contains about $10^{22}/m^3$ traps, would not provide space-charge limited current and that a trap-density of $10^{18}/m^3$ or less would be necessary for observation of the s.c.l. current. However, Longini and

12

Green[54] have shown that auto-compensation of deep-lying traps is possible under suitable conditions of crystal growth. According to this mechanism, deep electron traps, formed in the growing crystal, are compensated by shallow donor impurities having energy levels just below the conduction band. This may be illustrated by reference to cadmium sulphide. Copper is a frequent impurity, entering the lattice substitutionally as a Cu^{++} ion. However, the ion has 9 electrons in its 3d shell in the doubly-ionized state and it prefers to complete the shell by capture of an electron if possible. The energy level corresponding to this electron lies about 0·95 eV below the conduction band in CdS. Now a halogen, such as chlorine, may substitute for sulphur in the lattice and corresponds to a donor impurity having an energy level just below the conduction band. The electron from the Cl^- ion goes into the deep trapping-level of the copper thereby 'filling' the trap. There is experimental evidence that the chlorine will be taken up by the CdS crystal until the deep traps are nearly compensated, the balance of unfilled traps being in the region of $10^{18}/m^3$ or less.

Returning to the question of contacts, when a metal having a large number of free electrons is in contact with the insulator, the energy levels adjoin so that the Fermi levels are common to the two materials. In CdS, for instance, the Fermi level is 0·71 eV below the conduction band, so that the free electrons in the metal would have to acquire at least 0·7 eV of additional energy in order to be injected into the crystal. By special treatment of the crystal surface, and by use of a suitable metal, this can be overcome. In the case of work by Page et al.[55] the crystal surface is discharge cleaned, in a vacuum, by ion bombardment and an indium contact is applied by heating the crystal. It appears that the discharge cleaning may deplete the surface of sulphur leaving a layer of positively charged Cd ions. The indium diffuses into this layer, and it may be postulated that the effective contact potential barrier is replaced by a dipole layer through which the electrons can penetrate into the crystal. The blocking contact is made by depositing a high-work-function metal on to the crystal; tellurium is the most effective, but gold is often used.

When charge carriers are copiously released into the crystal, the unidirectional current flow is limited by the space-charge created.

The potential distribution resulting must obey Poisson's relation given in equation (1.26)

$$\nabla^2 \phi = -\rho/\epsilon \qquad (10.7)$$

where the charge density ρ is a function of position.

Similarly the equation of current continuity must be obeyed, i.e.

$$(\nabla \cdot \mathbf{J})\, dS = -\frac{\partial \rho}{\partial t}\, dS \qquad (10.8)$$

for any volume element dS. For steady-state conditions in which the space-charge density is constant, $\partial \rho / \partial t = 0$ and equation (10.8) states that the current density is also constant. It will therefore be given by

$$\mathbf{J} = \rho v \qquad (10.9)$$

where v is the drift velocity in the direction of the field.

We assume a geometrically simple configuration of a rectangular slab of dielectric, thickness d, with plane parallel electrodes on opposite faces, and a voltage V_0 applied to the anode (blocking) electrode with respect to the cathode (injecting) electrode. With this geometry, assuming trapping negligible, Poisson's equation simplifies to

$$\frac{\partial^2 V}{\partial z^2} = -\frac{\partial E}{\partial x} = -\rho/\epsilon. \qquad (10.10)$$

This differential equation may be solved using (10.9) provided that an expression for the drift velocity v in terms of applied voltage is obtained. In the case of the vacuum diode the required relation is easily obtained by equating the kinetic energy of the electrons to the accelerating force ($\frac{1}{2}mv^2 = Ve$), neglecting the thermal velocities of the emitted electrons. In the case of a crystal, however, the mean thermal energy of the space charge is greater than the energy gained from the electric field, since continuous collisions with the lattice tend to dissipate the latter. This difficulty is met by defining a mobility for the current carriers, as is done in semiconductors, given by μ, the drift velocity per unit field. Thus we write

$$v = \mu E. \qquad (10.11)$$

Using (10.11) with (10.10) and (10.9) we have

$$\frac{d^2 V}{dx^2} = -\frac{dE}{dx} = \frac{J}{\epsilon\mu E} = -\frac{J}{\epsilon\mu}\frac{dx}{dV}. \tag{10.12}$$

Multiplying through by dV we have

$$\frac{dE}{dx}dV = \frac{dV}{dx}dE = -EdE = -\frac{J}{\epsilon\mu}dx. \tag{10.13}$$

Integrating leads to

$$\frac{E^2}{2} = \frac{Jx}{\epsilon\mu} + C_1. \tag{10.14}$$

Now if we assume electrons are injected from the cathode at zero velocity, then $E = 0$ at $z = 0$ and so $C_1 = 0$. Thus, from (10.14),

$$\left(\frac{dV}{dx}\right)^2 = \frac{2Jx}{\epsilon\mu}.$$

i.e.
$$\int_0^{v_0} dV = \sqrt{\left(\frac{2J}{\epsilon\mu}\right)} \int_0^d x^{1/2}\,dx \tag{10.15}$$

we obtain

$$J = \frac{9}{8}\epsilon\mu\frac{V_0^2}{d^3}. \tag{10.16}$$

Thus, for space-charge-limited conditions the current density is proportional to the square of the applied voltage, in contrast to the familiar $J = CV_0^{3/2}$, the Child-Langmuir law for a thermionic diode. This square-law relationship has been confirmed experimentally by Page *et al.*, using a CdS crystal with an indium cathode and a gold anode.

Whilst the semiconductor diode is capable of operation at very high current densities, it is noisy and temperature-sensitive. The dielectric diode operates at much lower current densities but is relatively insensitive to temperature and should possess an inherently low noise figure. Since the conduction mechanism is the same as in an ordinary diode, it should be capable of operation up to very high frequencies. Shao and Wright[56] have reported measurements up to 900 Mc/s on s.c.l. cadmium sulphide diodes.

The development of a dielectric triode is the obvious next step and a great deal of work is being done in an attempt to realize a practical device. The major difficulty is to find means of introducing a control grid into the crystal. Limited success has been achieved with a construction employing a point contact near to the cathode, which modifies the field in the cathode region. Mutual conductances achieved have, however, been small. There seems no doubt that the problem will eventually be solved and, for low power applications, the dielectric triode will offer a low-noise, temperature-stable alternative to the transistor, especially for very high frequency operation.

References

[1] A. VON HIPPEL, (1952), *Dielectrics and Waves*, John Wiley (New York).

[2] K. S. COLE and R. H. COLE, (1942), *J. Chem. Phys.*, **10**, 98.

[3] L. HARTSHORN and W. H. WARD, (1936), *J. Instn. Elect. Engrs.*, **79**, 597.

[4] A. VON HIPPEL, (1954), *Dielectric Materials and Applications*, John Wiley (New York).

[5] B. ICHIJO, (1953), *J. Appl. Phys.* **24**, 307.

[6] E. FATUZZO, (1962), *Proc. Instn. Elect. Engrs.*, **109**C, 283.

[7] A. LURIO and E. STERN, (1960), *J. Appl. Phys.*, **31**, 1805.

[8] F. HORNER, T. A. TAYLOR, R. DUNSMUIR, J. LAMB and WILLIS JACKSON, (1946), *J. Instn. Elect. Engrs.*, **93**, Part III, 53.

[9] R. M. BOZORTH, (1959), *Ferromagnetism*, Van Nostrand (New York). p. 849

[10] H. M. BARLOW and A. L. CULLEN, (1950), *Microwave Measurements*, Constable.

[11] J. H. VAN VLECK, (1932), *The Theory of Electric and Magnetic Susceptibility*, Oxford University Press, p. 204.

[12] P. DEBYE, (1929), *Polar Molecules* (New York).

[13] D. H. WHIFFEN and H. W. THOMPSON, (1946), *Trans. Faraday Soc.*, **42A**, 114.

[14] K. S. COLE and R. H. COLE, (1941), *J. Chem. Phys.* **9**, 341.

[15] P. W. DAVIDSON and R. H. COLE, (1952), *J. Chem. Phys.*, **19**, 1484.

[16] B. K. P. SCAIFE, (1963), *Proc. Phys. Soc. Lond.*, **81**, 124.

[17] L. ONSAGER, (1936), *J. Amer. Chem. Soc.*, **58**.

[18] P. D. WILMOT, (Jan. 7, 1955), *Electrical Review*.

[19] J. G. KIRKWOOD, (1939), *J. Chem. Phys.* **7**, 911.

[20] H. FRÖHLICH, (1958), *Theory of Dielectrics*, Oxford University Press.

[21] H. A. KRAMERS and W. HEISENBERG, (1925), *Z. Phys.*, **31**, 681.

[22] L. HARTSHORN and J. A. SAXTON, (1958), *Handbuch der Physik*, **XVI**, 640.

[23] H. FRÖHLICH, (1939), *Rep. Phys. Soc. Progr. Phys.*, **6**, 411.

[24] See, for instance, HUME-ROTHERY, *Atomic Theory for Students in Metallurgy*, Institute of Metals, reprinted 1961.

[25] S. WHITEHEAD, (1951), *Dielectric Breakdown of Solids*, Oxford, Clarendon Press.

[26] A. VON HIPPEL and G. M. LEE, (1941), *Phys. Rev.*, **59**, 824.

[27] A. VON HIPPEL, (1932), *Z. Phys.*, **75**, 145; (1939), **88**, 352.

[28] G. A. VOROB'EV, (1957), *Soviet Tech. Phys.*, **1**, 322, 324.

[29] A. VON HIPPEL and R. J. MAURER, (1941), *Phys. Rev.*, **59**, 820.

[30] J. H. CALDERWOOD, R. COOPER and A. A. WALLACE, (1953), *Proc. Instn. Elect. Engrs.*, **100**, 11A, 105.

[31] H. C. HALL and R. M. RUSSEK, (1954), *Proc. Instn. Elect. Engrs.*, **101**, Pt. 2, 47.

[32] J. H. MASON, (1951), *Proc. Instn. Elect. Engrs.*, **98**, Pt. 1, 44.

[33] J. H. MASON, (1959), *Progress in Dielectrics*, Vol. I, Heywood.

[34] T. J. LEWIS, (1960), *J. Electrochem. Soc.*, **107**, 185; (1959), *Progress in Dielectrics*, Vol. I, Heywood, p. 97.

[35] K. C. KAO, (1962), *Trans. Amer. Instn. Elect. Engrs.*

[36] A. H. SHARBAUGH and P. K. WATSON, (1962), *Progress in Dielectrics*, Vol. 4, Heywood, p. 199.

[37] See, for instance, P. W. MASON, (1950), *Piezoelectric Crystals and Their Application to Ultrasonics*, Van Nostrand (New York); P. W. FORSBERGH, (1956), *Handbuch der Physik*, **17**.

[38] A. VON HIPPEL, (1952), *Dielectrics and Waves*, John Wiley (New York), p. 199 *et seq.*

[39] C. B. SAWYER and C. H. TOWER, (1930), *Phys. Rev.*, **35**, 269.

[40] W. J. MERZ, (1962), *Progress in Dielectrics*, Vol. 4, Heywood, p. 105.

[41] W. KÄNZIG, (1957), *Solid State Physics*, **4**, 6.

[42] C. KITTEL, (1951), *Phys. Rev.*, **82**, 729.

[43] G. SHIRANE, E. SAWAGUCHI and Y. TAKAGI, (1951), *Phys. Rev.*, **84**, 476.

[44] G. L. PEARSON and W. L. FELDMAN, (1959), *J. Phys. Chem. Solids*, **9**, 28.

[45] P. W. FORSBERGH, JR., (1956), *Handbuch der Physik*, **17**, p. 340 *et seq*.

[46] C. A. ROSEN, (1956), *Ceramic Transformers and Filters*, Ph.D. thesis, Syracuse University.

[47] W. P. MASON, (1948), *Electrochemical Transducers and Wave filters*, Van Nostrand (New York), 2nd Ed.

[48] D. S. CAMPBELL and A. M. MACSWAN, (1962), *Proc. Instn. Elect. Engrs.*, **109B**, 374.

[49] J. HARTMANN and B. TROLLE, (1939), *J. Sci. Instrum.*, **16**, 140.

[50] A. E. CRAWFORD, (1955), *Ultrasonic Engineering*, Butterworth.

[51] A. SILVERSTEIN, (1954), *Electronics*, **27**, 150.

[52] A. ROSE, (1955), *Phys. Rev.*, **97**, 1538.

[53] M. A. LAMPERT, (1950), *Phys. Rev.*, **103**, 1648.

[54] R. L. LONGINI and R. F. GREENE, (1956), *Phys. Rev.*, **109**, 992.

[55] D. S. PAGE, A. A. KAYALI and G. T. WRIGHT, (1962), **80**, 1133.

[56] J. SHAO and G. T. WRIGHT, (1961), *Solid State Electronics*, **3**, 291.

Subject Index

Author Index